GONE WITH THE KUDZU

GONE WITH THE KUDZU

DOUG MARLETTE

RUTLEDGE HILL PRESS
NASHVILLE, TENNESSEE

All of the cartoons that appear in this work have been previously published in various newspapers. "Kudzu" is distributed by Creators Syndicate, Inc.

Published in Nashville, Tennessee, by Rutledge Hill Press, Inc., 211 Seventh Avenue North, Nashville, Tennessee 37219.
Distributed in Canada by H. B. Fenn & Company, Ltd., 1090 Lorimar Drive, Mississauga, Ontario, L5S 1R7.

Library of Congress Cataloging-in-Publication Data

Marlette, Doug, 1949–
   [Kudzu. Selections]
   Gone with the Kudzu / Doug Marlette.
      p.   cm.
   ISBN 1-55853-336-2 (pbk.)
   I. Title.
PN6727.K8M37   1995
741.5'973—dc20   95-6071
                                                CIP

Printed in the United States of America
1 2 3 4 5 6 7—99 98 97 96 95

PREACHER, I'M AT MY WIT'S END WITH MY BOY, KUDZU!...

I FEAR MY PARENTING SKILLS JUST AREN'T WHAT THEY SHOULD BE!...

MARLETTE

...IN FACT, SOMETIMES I FEEL LIKE A COMPLETE FAILURE AT PARENTING!...

MRS. DUBOSE, I'M SURE YOUR PARENTING IS FINE...

...BUT EVEN THE BEST OF PARENTING...

... IS NO MATCH FOR ORDINARY TEENAGERING!

5

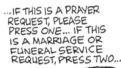

9

...AND NOW TO SLICK SLADE HIGH ABOVE THE BYPASS METROPOLITAN AREA...

...WE HAVE NO TRAFFIC ON THE UNPAVED ROADS OUT IN THE COUNTY...

...THERE'S A DODGE DART PARKED OUTSIDE THE BYPASS SEED 'N' FEED...

...WE HAVE A RED PICK-UP TURNING AROUND IN THE BAPTIST CHURCH PARKING LOT...

...AND THE CAUTION LIGHT IN FRONT OF DHB'S SERVICE STATION IS STILL BROKE SO Y'ALL TAKE IT EASY...

...THERE'S A JOHN DEERE TRACTOR MAKIN' IT'S WAY THROUGH TOWN WHICH MIGHT TIE UP TRAFFIC SO ALL YOU RUSH HOUR COMMUTERS TRY TO AVOID MAIN STREET, Y'HEAR!...

I DON'T KNOW WHAT I'D DO WITHOUT THE CHOPPER ONE SKYCAM TRAFFIC REPORT!

PREACHER, I'M WORRIED ABOUT MAMA — SHE'S BEEN SO MOODY LATELY! I THINK SHE NEEDS A HOBBY... SOME OUTLET FOR HER ENERGY...

HOW ABOUT HER OWN TV SHOW? I KNOW WHEN I'M FEELING OUT-OF-SORTS, A LITTLE ON-CAMERA WORK IS A PICK-ME-UP!

GOSH, HER OWN TV SPOT — I WAS THINKING MORE ALONG THE LINES OF QUILTING BEES OR MACRAME OR DABBLING IN REAL ESTATE!..

THERE'S NOTHING WRONG WITH YOUR MAMA THAT A FEW MINUTES ON THE AIR WON'T CURE!

...OR ELECTRO-SHOCK THERAPY!

DON'T BE SILLY!

IT'S TRUE, MAMA — PREACHER WANTS TO PUT YOU ON HIS SHOW!

WHAT WOULD I DO ON TELEVISION?

ANYTHING YOU WANT — HE'S GIVING YOU A THREE-MINUTE GUEST SPOT TO DO WITH AS YOU WISH!

BUT-BUT I HAVE NO EXPERIENCE!... I HAVE NOTHING TO WEAR!... I-I'D FALL APART! I'M TOO SHY!

IT WOULD EAT 'EM UP WITH JEALOUSY AT THE LADIES MISSIONARY AUXILIARY!

DO I GET MY OWN DRESSING ROOM?

...AND NOW WE PRESENT A BRAND-NEW FEATURE ON THE WILL B. DUNN SHOW: "A MOMENT WITH MAMA"!

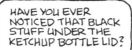

HAVE YOU EVER NOTICED THAT BLACK STUFF UNDER THE KETCHUP BOTTLE LID?

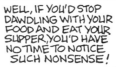

WELL, IF YOU'D STOP DAWDLING WITH YOUR FOOD AND EAT YOUR SUPPER, YOU'D HAVE NO TIME TO NOTICE SUCH NONSENSE!

I'M MAMA DUBOSE — AND DON'T FORGET TO EAT YOUR GREENS!

KUDZU, LOOK — YOUR MAMA'S SEGMENT IS ON TV!

HI — I'M MAMA DUBOSE...

... I KNOW I'M NOT AS INTERESTING AS THE USUAL SEX AND VIOLENCE YOU GET ON TV ...

NO — GO AHEAD... TURN THE CHANNEL... I UNDERSTAND... I'LL JUST SIT HERE IN THE DARK TALKING TO MYSELF...

I'M USED TO IT BY NOW.. MY SON PAYS NO ATTENTION TO ME EITHER...

HMM... GUILT-TV!

14

THE WILL B. DUNN SHOW

AND NOW HERE'S OUR NEW *MEDIA CRITIC,* NASAL T. LARDBOTTOM!

IF I REMEMBER CORRECTLY THE *PERSIAN GULF WAR* HAD IT'S OWN LOGO ON *CNN...*

...YET THE *CLARENCE THOMAS* CONFIRMATION HEARINGS DID NOT!... NOR DID THE *WILLIAM KENNEDY SMITH* TRIAL... NOR DID THE *MIKE TYSON* TRIAL... NOR DID THE *BILL CLINTON-GENNIFER FLOWERS* EPISODE!...

WHERE ARE OUR VALUES?!...WHAT ARE WE TEACHING OUR CHILDREN?!...WHAT DOES THIS SAY ABOUT US AS A PEOPLE!

...UNTIL WE GIVE TASTELESS SEX THE SAME DIGNITY AND RESPECT WE RESERVE FOR *MINDLESS VIOLENCE* WE HAVE NO ONE TO BLAME BUT...

...THE JAPANESE!

SOMEBODY HAD TO SAY IT!

Panel 1: DO YOU SUPPOSE YOU'LL NEED ANY SALT ON THOSE POTATOES, SON? / OH, NO, MA'AM.

Panel 2: I SEE.

Panel 3: OH. DO YOU WANT ME TO PASS THE SALT? / PLEASE.

Panel 4: MAMA HAS ELEVATED *PASSIVE AGGRESSION* TO AN ART FORM!

Modern Depression — Iron Nathan — SELF-HELP SHAMAN — "I'M O.K.— YOU'RE DOG MEAT!" — THE ROAD LESS POTHOLED

Nathan Goodvibes, PhD. NOTED SECULAR HUMANIST, HIGH SCHOOL GUIDANCE COUNSELOR AND BEST-SELLING AUTHOR OF THE MEN'S MOVEMENT BIBLE "IRON NATHAN" NOW WRITES AN ADVICE COLUMN FOR "MODERN DEPRESSION"—

Dear Mr. Goodvibes,

I have lost the will to live. What now? Blue

Dear Blue, Whenever I lose the will to live I always look in the last place I remember having it...

Dear Mr. Goodvibes, I can't hide my depression any longer.

I had my "colors" done recently...

...and when I asked if I was a "spring", "summer" or "fall" person...

I was told I'm a "Nuclear Winter"!

Dear Mr. Goodvibes, Although you seem a little schizoid to me...

...thank you for always being there for me.

...And there, and there, and way over there!

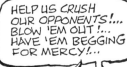

19

BILL CLINTON CAMPAIGNS FOR THE COVETED *DUB DUBOSE* VOTE:

LET ME TAKE A MOMENT TO EXPLAIN MY SMALL FILLIN' STATION OWNER SUBSIDY PLAN...

LATER...
...AND THE SAVINGS WOULD BE PLOWED BACK INTO THE HEALTH-CARE PLAN ALONG WITH THE PEACE DIVIDEND AND MY DAUGHTER CHELSEA'S ALLOWANCE.

SECRETARY OF BARBECUE! HOW DOES THAT SOUND?

ROSS PEROT CAMPAIGNS FOR DUB'S VOTE!
A HUNDRED DOLLARS, TAKE IT OR LEAVE IT!

A THOUSAND SMACKERS, THAT'S AS HIGH AS I GO!

TEN GRAND AND AMBASSADOR TO SOMALIA!

OKAY!...OKAY!... YOU DRIVE A TOUGH BARGAIN! ...I PROMISE NOT TO PLACE YOU UNDER SURVEILLANCE!

I PROMISE TO MAKE "ACHY-BREAKY HEART" THE NATIONAL ANTHEM!
GROAN

I OPPOSE A TAX ON MUDFLAPS!

IF GUNRACKS ARE OUTLAWED, ONLY OUTLAWS WILL OWN GUN RACKS!

BARBECUE ON DEMAND!

THE CANDIDATES WOO DUB!

PREACHER, THE PRESIDENT'S OFFERED DUB A SEAT ON THE SUPREME COURT AND CLINTON SAYS HE'LL APPOINT HIM SECRETARY OF BARBECUE!
DO NOT DISTURB

HILLARY EVEN BAKED DUB SOME *COOKIES!*
SO?
SO WHAT IF THEIR BRIBES WORK?! AREN'T YOU WORRIED?!

LET 'EM BRIBE AWAY! ANYBODY WHO KNOWS DUB KNOWS IF YOU WANTA GET TO *DUB DUBOSE* YOU GOTTA GET TO MAYBELLE!
MAYBELLE?...

HIS WIFE?!
HIS DOG!
STAY TUNED...

21

As DUB DUBOSE GOES, SO GOES THE COUNTRY — AND THE CANDIDATES CAMPAIGN HARD IN BYPASS:

BARBECUE! GRITS! MUD FLAPS!

...BUT NONE SEEM TO KNOW WHAT WILL B. DUNN KNOWS:

FAUX BUBBAS EVERY ONE OF 'EM!... WEEKEND BILLYBOBS!

...AND IF THERE'S ONE THING A *TRUE BUBBA* LIKE DUB CAN'T STAND, IT'S A COUNTERFEIT CRACKER!

THERE'S ONLY ONE WAY TO *HIS* HEART AND VOTE...

...HIS PRECIOUS MAYBELLE!

DUB DUBOSE IS THE KEY TO THIS ELECTION

HE'S THE SWING VOTE INCARNATE ALL RIGHT!

...AND THE KEY TO DUB DUBOSE IS MAYBELLE!

HIS DOG?

THAT'S RIGHT — IF DUB HASN'T MADE UP HIS MIND BY *CRUNCH TIME*, HE'LL GO WITH *MAYBELLE!* WHOEVER SHE PREFERS!

YIKES!

DO YOU MEAN A MANGY *YELLOW DOG* HOLDS THE FUTURE OF THIS COUNTRY IN ITS FLEA-BITTEN PAWS?!

THANK THE LORD!

NOTICE HOW THE OTHER CANDIDATES WORK ON DUB AND IGNORE HIS BELOVED HOUND DOG MAYBELLE...

NOT WILL B. DUNN.

HERE MAYBELLE— HAVE A DOGGIE BISCUIT!

I BEEN PUMPIN' HER WITH GOODIES FOR WEEKS NOW...

COME ELECTION DAY, WHEN *DUB* TAKES MAYBELLE WITH HIM TO VOTE, WILL B. DUNN'S GONNA WIN THE ONLY *POLL THAT COUNTS!*

⊙CTOBER SURPRISE!

WHAT THE SO-CALLED EXPERTS OVERLOOKED IS *DUB'S* DOG MAYBELLE!

"IF *DUB DUBOSE* IS UNDECIDED ON ELECTION DAY...

...HE TAKES MAYBELLE TO THE POLLS WITH HIM... CARRIES HER RIGHT INTO THE VOTING BOOTH..."

...LET'S HER SNIFF THE BALLOT..."

"...AND MAKE THE CALL!"

AARROOOOOO!

22

TROMP TROMP TROMP TROMP

AARRRRGH!

SO MUCH FOR LOSING GRACEFULLY!

A BITTER WILL B. DUNN BROODS OVER HIS ELECTION DISASTER:

HOLY CATFISH! I GOT LESS THAN ONE-TENTH OF ONE PERCENT OF THE VOTE!

SADDAM HUSSEIN WOULD DO BETTER THAN THAT!

...AND WHAT REALLY HURTS IS THEY'RE SAYING REGISTRATION AND TURN-OUT WERE UP BECAUSE FOLKS WANTED TO VOTE AGAINST THE TELEVANGELIST!

OH, THAT'S CRUEL! A LOT OF VOTERS COULD CARE LESS IF YOU WERE IN THE RACE!

Dear Mr. Goodvibes, What is it now with this advice column?

Still trying to get Mommy's attention, huh? The college degrees, the books you write, and now this!...
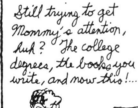

Nothing's ever enough. You're still desperate for her approval, aren't you?...

DARN IT! I TOLD MY SHRINK NEVER TO WRITE ME AT THE OFFICE!

Dear Mr. Goodvibes,

How do you get up in the morning?
Bummed

Dear Bummed, The same way I get up in the evening:

...Lithium.

24

25

HI, VERANDA! WELCOME!

HELLO, IDA MAE—WHAT ARE *YOU* DOING HERE?

I'M PRESIDENT—THIS IS *FUTURE HOMEMAKERS OF AMERICA*

FUTURE HOMEMAKERS?! I'M IN THE WRONG PLACE.

I WANTED *FUTURE HOMEWRECKERS!*

WOMEN'S ROLES ARE CHANGING, MR. GOODVIBES! I'VE CHANGED MY MIND ABOUT MY CAREER AGAIN!

IT'S CALLED *PERSONAL GROWTH*, DEAR.

AS YOU KNOW, I USED TO WANT TO BECOME A *DALLAS COWGIRL*... THEN A TV GAME SHOW HOSTESS...

BUT NOW I'VE RAISED MY SIGHTS! I WANT A CAREER THAT FULLY UTILIZES MY SKILLS AND TALENTS! A POSITION THAT PAYS WELL, HAS GLAMOUR PLUS JOB SECURITY!

GOOD FOR YOU, VERANDA!... WHAT'S THAT?!

THE *OTHER WOMAN!*

HOLY CATFISH, GIRL! YOU MEAN TO TELL ME YOU ASPIRE TO BE A WANTON WOMAN!...A...A HOMEWRECKER!?!

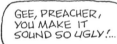

GEE, PREACHER, YOU MAKE IT SOUND SO *UGLY!*...

IT *IS* UGLY, YOUNG LADY!... IT'S *ADULTERY!*

REV. WILL B. DUNN COUNSELOR

WELL, AFTER ALL, PREACHER, I AM AN *ADULT!*

REV. WILL B. DUNN COUNSELOR

PREACHER, I CAME TO YOU IN GOOD FAITH SEEKING SUPPORT AND GUIDANCE FOR MY *OTHER WOMAN* CAREER GOALS AND YOU'RE TREATING IT AS IF HOMEWRECKING IS SOMETHING CHEAP AND TAWDRY!

I'M SORRY, VERANDA, BUT IT'S ADULTERY, AND IT'S A SIN!

AND YOU CALL YOURSELF A COUNSELOR!

WELL, IT'S CERTAINLY AN UNUSUAL "LIFESTYLE", BUT WHO AM I TO JUDGE?!

THANK GOD FOR *SECULAR HUMANISTS!*

GOODVIBES COOL GUIDANCE COUNSELOR

VERANDA, ARE YOU IN LOVE WITH SKIPPER STUDLEY?
LOVE?
I THINK THE WORLD OF SKIPPER, I DO...
I THINK HE'D MAKE A WONDERFUL *FIRST HUSBAND*!
MARLETTE

HOLY CATFISH! I GOT HIT WITH ANOTHER TECHNICAL IN CHURCH LEAGUE BASKETBALL!...
HOLY ROLLERS
THE REFS ARE DISCRIMINATING AGAINST US *PROTESTANTS*!
MARLETTE
IF THE CATHOLICS CAN MAKE THE SIGN OF THE CROSS BEFORE EACH *FREE THROW*...
I DON'T SEE WHY I CAN'T HANDLE SNAKES!
HOLY ROLLERS

WOE UNTO YE HYPOCRITES!
BROOD OF VIPERS!
MARLETTE
WICKED AND ADULTEROUS GENERATION!
MARLETTE
I LOVE TALKING TRASH IN CHURCH LEAGUE BASKETBALL!
HOLY ROLLERS

WE REALLY HAMMERED *FIRST FUNDAMENTALIST* IN THE CHURCH LEAGUE BASKETBALL TOURNAMENT!
MARLETTE
I TOTALLY SHUT DOWN THEIR HOT-SHOT POINT GUARD!... HELD HIM SCORELESS!...
YOU WERE REALLY TALKING SOME TRASH! WHAT WERE YOU SAYING?
NOTHING MUCH!
JUST THAT HE'D BURN IN HELL IF HE SCORED ON ME!

31

FRANKLY, PREACHER, I'M SHOCKED AT SOME OF THESE BIBLE STORIES YOU ASSIGNED THE KIDDIES IN SUNDAY SCHOOL...

SOME OF THESE IMAGES ARE SO VIOLENT AND TERRIFYING, I'M AFRAID THEY MIGHT TRAUMATIZE THE YOUNGSTERS...

...SO I'VE TAKEN THE LIBERTY OF EDITING THEM!...

EDITING THEM?

FOR INSTANCE: "DANIEL IN THE DEN OF LIONS"...

WHAT ABOUT IT?

I CHANGED IT TO "DANIEL IN THE PETTING ZOO"!

"DANIEL IN THE PETTING ZOO"?!

YES, "DANIEL IN THE DEN OF LIONS" IS TOO SCARY FOR YOUNG CHILDREN...

...AND THIS STORY ABOUT "SHADRACH, MESHACH, AND ABEDNEGO IN THE FIERY FURNACE!...

WHAT'S WRONG WITH IT?

REALLY, PREACHER...

COULDN'T THE POINT BE MADE JUST AS EFFECTIVELY IF SHADRACH, MESHACH AND ABEDNEGO WERE IN A SAUNA?!

LET ME GET THIS STRAIGHT: YOU WANT DANIEL IN A PETTING ZOO — NOT A LION'S DEN!...

...AND SHADRACH, MESHACH AND ABEDNEGO IN A SAUNA — NOT A FIERY FURNACE!

YES, AND THIS BUSINESS ABOUT GOD TELLING ABRAHAM TO SACRIFICE HIS SON?!...

WHAT OF IT?

GROSS!

CAN'T WE HAVE GOD TELLING ABRAHAM TO GROUND HIS SON FOR TWO WEEKS WITH NO VIDEO GAME PRIVILEGES!?!

...AND NOW FOR MY IMPRESSION OF AN OSTRICH!

BONK!

NEVER TRY TO BURY YOUR HEAD IN THE PERCH!

I'LL BE FRANK WITH YOU, PREACHER— I'M A FEMINIST SO I HAD MY DOUBTS ABOUT HAVING A MAN MARRY US!

I WANTED A FEMALE MINISTER, BUT THE WOMEN IN THE CHURCH REASSURED ME ...

THAT I WAS SENSITIVE TO WOMEN'S ISSUES...

THAT YOU WERE A SISSY!

PREACHER, MY WIFE AND I WANT TO RENEW OUR VOWS!

AWW, HOW SWEET! IN THIS DAY AND AGE! AND YOU WANT ME TO REMARRY YOU!?!

UH-HUH!

...BUT TO DIFFERENT SPOUSES!

OLD LADY BASCOMB WAS THE UGLIEST WOMAN IN TOWN— A REAL BOW WOW!..

PREACHER, WHAT A TERRIBLE AND CRUEL THING TO SAY ABOUT NETTIE BASCOMB!

ARE YOU WITH THE FAMILY?...

NO, THE A.S.P.C.A.!

Dear Preacher, Why are so many self-help gurus so personally screwed up? Amazed

Dear Amazed, Remember the first rule of modern therapy:

"Snow thyself."

Kudzu by Doug Marlette

Tell It To The Preacher

Dear Preacher,
I am ready to join a religious cult or sect.

Any advice?
Pilgrim

Dear Pilgrim,

Historically, many religious cults and sects have encouraged unhealthy fanaticism, even Holy Wars...

If you're going to practice a religion remember:

Practice Safe Sects!

BREEP!

DORIS, THIS IS YOUR INSTINCTS CALLING FOR THE UMPTEENTH TIME!...

...IT'S TIME TO FLY SOUTH FOR THE WINTER, OKAY? 'BYE!

I ALWAYS LET MY ANSWERING MACHINE SCREEN THE CALL-OF-THE-WILD!

WOODY ALLEN'S ANALYST CAME TO ME AFTER THE WOODY-M/A THING BLEW UP!...

HE FELT HUMILIATED... HELD UP TO NATIONAL SCORN... HE JUST NEEDED SOMEBODY TO TALK TO...

I TOLD HIM THERAPY WAS NO PANACEA... NO CURE-ALL...

HE SAID I WAS TELLING NOAH ABOUT THE FLOOD!

HOW'S WOODY ALLEN'S SHRINK DOING IN THERAPY?

HE'S BITTER AND DISILLUSIONED... HE DROP-KICKED WOODY OUT OF ANALYSIS...

HE'S THINKING OF CHANGING CAREERS— GOING INTO A LINE OF WORK THAT ACTUALLY HELPS PEOPLE!...

LIKE WHAT?

COMEDY.

REWIND WITH ME NOW, IF YOU WILL, TO THE LORD'S PROMISE TO THE CHILDREN OF ISRAEL...

...THEN FAST FORWARD TO PAUL'S LETTER TO THE CORINTHIANS...

...NOW FREEZE FRAME AND LET'S SLO-MO THROUGH THAT VERSE ONCE AGAIN!

I TRY TO RELATE TO OUR YOUNG PEOPLE!

37

MR. GOODVIBES SAYS THERE ARE TWO KINDS OF PEOPLE: *TYPE A PERSONALITIES* AND *TYPE B.*

MR. GOODVIBES IS PARTIALLY RIGHT... THERE ARE TWO KINDS OF PEOPLE...

PEOPLE WHO DIVIDE HUMANITY INTO TWO KINDS, AND THOSE WHO DON'T!

MARLETTE

WHAT'S THIS?

A GIFT TO CHEER YOU UP!

YOU'VE BEEN SO DOWN SINCE YOUR ELECTION DISASTER I THOUGHT YOU MIGHT ENJOY A SUBSCRIPTION TO *MODERN DEPRESSION*...

MARLETTE

"...A JOURNAL OF *POETRY* AND *PROZAC.*"

I KNOW HOW MISERY LOVES COMPANY!

THERE'S EVEN AN ADVICE COLUMN BY YOUR ARCH-RIVAL IN HUMAN RELATIONS, MR. GOODVIBES!

OOOH, BUMMER!

LORD, I DON'T ASK FOR ANYTHING THAT'S NOT COMING TO ME...

ALL I WANT ARE MY JUST DESSERTS!

SPLAT!

LET ME REPHRASE THAT!

MARLETTE

AT LAST—AN *EXERCISE MACHINE* I CAN LIVE WITH!

MARLETTE

NORDIC PERCH!

WELL, PREACHER, AREN'T YOU GOING TO CONGRATULATE ME ON MY NEW ADVICE COLUMN IN "MODERN DEPRESSION"?..

BIG DEAL!

DO I DETECT A NOTE OF JEALOUSY BECAUSE MY ADVICE IS MORE WIDELY HEEDED THAN YOURS?

FAT CHANCE!

ISN'T ENVY ONE OF THE SEVEN DEADLY SINS?

AND PRIDE GOETH BEFORE A FALL!

I'LL HAVE YOU KNOW I'M TRAINED IN SENSITIVITY AND INSIGHT!

HERE'S AN INSIGHT FOR YOU, MR. PhDUH! BULL HOCKEY!

I FEEL SORRY FOR YOU, PREACHER — YOUR MEASLY LITTLE ADVICE COLUMN ONLY REACHES READERS HERE IN LITTLE OLD BYPASS...

...WHILE I CONNECT WITH KOOKS AND NUT CASES ALL OVER THE COUNTRY!

IT'S QUALITY, GOODVIBES — NOT QUANTITY!

...AND I'LL STACK UP MY WHINERS AND BELLYACHERS AGAINST YOURS ANY DAY!

I BET MINE ARE MORE DEPRESSED THAN YOURS!

IN THEIR DREAMS!

NO WAY! NO WAY! NO WAY!

WAY! WAY! WAY!

SELF-HELP GURUS ARE VERY COMPETITIVE!

Dear Mr. Goodvibes, You always talk about a positive attitude.

Well, I ran for President with a positive attitude and still lost. So much for your stupid advice. Bitter in Bypass

Dear Bitter, I never promised you a White House Rose Garden.

Dear Mr. Goodvibes, You get lots of letters from folks who say they're in a Black Hole of depression...

I bet my Black Hole is worse than theirs. Despondent

Dear Despondent, I don't like your Black Holier-Than-Thou attitude.

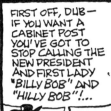
FIRST OFF, DUB— IF YOU WANT A CABINET POST YOU'VE GOT TO STOP CALLING THE NEW PRESIDENT AND FIRST LADY "BILLY BOB" AND "HILLY BOB"!...

WHO SAYS I WANT ONE!

OF COURSE YOU DO— EVERYBODY WANTS TO BE A PART OF THE NEW TEAM!

IF THAT'S BILLY BOB, TELL HIM I AIN'T HERE!

HELLO?

DUB, IT'S HILLY BOB!... I MEAN MRS. CLINTON! SHE'S BAKED SOME COOKIES FOR YOU!

TELL HER I'M FULLER'N A TICK!

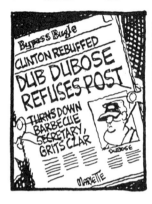
Bypass Bugle

CLINTON REBUFFED

DUB DUBOSE REFUSES POST

TURNS DOWN BARBECUE SECRETARY, GRITS CZAR

DUBOSE

UNCLE DUB, YOU'RE THE ONLY PERSON EVER TO TURN DOWN A JOB WITH THE NEW ADMINISTRATION... DO YOU REALIZE HOW THIS LOOKS?

YOU'RE THE PRESIDENT-ELECT'S FIRST CRISIS! HE'S NOT EVEN PRESIDENT YET, AND YOU'RE PERCEIVED AS HIS FIRST FAILURE!

DUB'S MAKING SERBIA LOOK EASY!

HONK!

DUB, IT'S CLINTON! HE'S HERE WITH A JOB OFFER!

I ALREADY GOT A JOB!

HE'S PULLING OUT ALL THE STOPS TO GET YOU ON BOARD! HE'S PUTTING HIS PRESTIGE ON THE LINE!

YOU CAN'T SAY "NO", DUB—HE BROUGHT HILLARY!... HE BROUGHT AL AND TIPPER! HE BROUGHT THE MEDIA!

HE—HE EVEN BROUGHT THE BUS!

I HEAR IT— IT NEEDS A TUNE-UP!

FORGET SECRETARY OF BARBECUE!... FORGET GRITS CZAR!... HOW DOES THIS SOUND: AMBASSADOR DUB DUBOSE!?!

AMBASSADOR? TO WHERE?

THE GREAT STATE OF NORTH CAROLINA!

NORTH CAROLINA?... MY HOME STATE?

THE ONLY SOUTHERN STATE OUR CAMPAIGN TARGETED AND DIDN'T WIN!

WE'RE TRYING TO RE-ESTABLISH DIPLOMATIC TIES! THAT'S WHERE YOU'D COME IN!

Panel 1: LET ME GET THIS STRAIGHT—YOU WANT TO APPOINT ME AMBASSADOR TO THE STATE OF *NORTH CAROLINA*?!

WE LOST THE STATE—NO NEED TO BURN BRIDGES!

Panel 2: IT MAKES SENSE— YOU'RE A NATIVE... YOU SPEAK THEIR LANGUAGE... YOU ALREADY LIVE THERE, SO THERE'S NO PAPERWORK!...

Panel 3: OF COURSE, THERE ARE RISKS: *TWO REPUBLICAN SENATORS*... *JESSE HELMS* COUNTRY...

Panel 4: YOU COULD BE TAKEN HOSTAGE—LET'S NOT SUGARCOAT IT!

Panel 5: IN PRESIDENT-ELECT BILL CLINTON'S FIRST TRANSITION SETBACK, FILLING STATION OWNER *DUB DUBOSE* HAS TURNED DOWN AN ADMINISTRATION JOB...

Panel 6: CLINTON PULLED OUT ALL THE STOPS, PUTTING MOST OF HIS PRE-INAUGURAL PRESTIGE ON THE LINE TO NO AVAIL...

WE BROUGHT ALONG THE BUS AND EVERY-THING...

Panel 7: ...EVEN MORE DEVAS-TATING TO THE PRESI-DENT-ELECT IS EVIDENCE THAT DUBOSE NEVER EVEN SUBMITTED A RESUME...

INCREDIBLE! HE HAS NO CONCERN FOR HIS *POLITICAL VIABILITY!*

Panel 8: ...SOURCES CLOSE TO DUBOSE SAY HE HAS A LONG HISTORY OF INTRANSIGENCE: I'VE NEVER SEEN HIM *NETWORK* A DAY IN HIS LIFE!

Panel 9: HOLY CATFISH!

Panel 10: I'M NOT SAYING I HAVE A *DUMB* CONGREGATION...

Panel 11: ...BUT THEY MOVE THEIR LIPS WHILE *WATCHING TV!*

Panel 12: THE DONALD TRUMP CASH FLOW WATCH:

OH, NO! HE'S BEEN BOUNCED OFF THE *FORBES 400!* VISA'S REVOKED HIS CREDIT CARD! HE'S SELLING THE *TRUMP PRINCESS!*

Panel 13: POOR DONALD!

POOR DONALD?! POOR MARLA!

Panel 14: SHE PICKED A LOSER! ONE DAY SHE'S ON TOP OF HER GAME AS THE *OTHER WOMAN*...THE NEXT SHE'S ON HER WAY TO BECOMING JUST ANOTHER *TROPHY WIFE!*

Panel 15: LIFE IS SO UNFAIR!

OVERNIGHT, SHE'S SUBJECT TO THE *OTHER WOMAN'S* WORST FEAR!

ANOTHER OTHER WOMAN!

PREACHER, WHAT IS THE MEANING OF LIFE?

SHUT UP, KUDZU!

WELL, *EXCUSE* ME FOR ASKING!

THAT'S OKAY— HOW WILL YOU LEARN IF YOU DON'T ASK?!

LEARN WHAT?

NOT TO ASK!

DUB, IF YOU WON'T *LOOK OUT* FOR YOURSELF, THINK OF YOUR *FRIENDS!* I COULD USE A CLINTON APPOINTMENT!

SECRETARY OF FAMILY VALUES! SECRETARY OF *TELEVANGELISM!* AMBASSADOR TO THE *VATICAN!*...

—FIRST BOZO!

ACTUALLY, CLINTON, GORE AND I SHARE THE SAME BAPTIST FAITH...

WE SHARE THE SAME THEOLOGY, WE SING THE SAME HYMNS, WE PRAY THE SAME PRAYERS...

MODESTY PREVENTS ME FROM OFFERING MY SERVICES AS WHITE HOUSE CHAPLAIN...

...BUT, DUB, PERHAPS YOU COULD...

I'M TOO MODEST, TOO, PREACHER!

DUB, YOU'RE MAKING THE *PRESIDENT-ELECT* LOOK BAD!

YOU'RE *RUINING* THE TRANSITION!

DUB'S THE FIRST LIVING ORGANISM TO WITHSTAND THE FULL, FLAT-OUT WATTAGE OF BILL CLINTON'S CHARM!

HE'S SCARY ALL RIGHT!

HE'S INCORRUPTIBLE! HE'S *UNREACHABLE!*

NOT *ENTIRELY!*

PREACHER HAS A SCHE...ER...VISION!

47

48

PREACHER DREAMS:

HOW WILL PRESIDENT CLINTON EVER REPAY ME FOR SOLVING HIS DUB CRISIS?

AMBASSADOR TO THE VATICAN?

COVERED-DISH SUPPERS ON THE WHITE HOUSE GROUNDS?

CONGRESSIONAL FOOTWASHINGS?

ROSE GARDEN WEDDINGS!

MASS BAPTISMS IN THE REFLECTING POOL?

SNAPPY STATE FUNERAL EULOGIES!

MARLETTE

WILL B. DUNN SPECULATES ON HIS FUTURE IN THE CLINTON ADMINISTRATION:

I SUPPOSE KNIGHTHOOD IS OUT OF THE QUESTION!

THE FIRST SOUTHERN BAPTIST POPE!

NAAA...

I HOPE HE DOESN'T ASK ME TO CAST DEMONS OUT OF CONGRESS!

BEEEP!

HELLO!

...AN INAUGURAL PRAYER?!!...

WHY, I'D BE PROUD TO!

MARLETTE

IT'S THE INAUGURATION PLANNING COMMITTEE!

JUST ONE SUGGESTION ABOUT YOUR INAUGURAL PRAYER, PREACHER...

GOOD—I'M WORKING ON IT AS WE SPEAK!

MARLETTE

KEEP IT SHORT!

INAUGURATION WEEK—WHILE WASHINGTON PARTIES DOWN, WILL B. DUNN IS ENSCONCED IN HIS HOTEL ROOM...

DON'T...STOP... ♪ THINKIN' ABOUT TO MORROW...

...WORKING FEVERISHLY ON THE LAST MINUTE DETAILS OF HIS INAUGURAL PRAYER:

BLESS THE HORS D'OEUVRES... BLESS THE HIGH SCHOOL MARCHING BANDS... BLESS THE SCAFFOLDING... BLESS THE PRESIDENTIAL SAX...

BLESS TIPPER'S HAIRDO... BLESS THE BEAN COUNTERS, THE POLICY WONKS AND THE SUCK-UPS... BLESS C-SPAN AND NPR...

BLESS THE RAZORBACKS, THE PASSED OVER AND THE OVERLOOKED,... BLESS THE HOMEBOYS AND FAUX BUBBAS, THE INSIDERS AND OUT-SIDERS...BLESS BILL AND HILLARY, CHELSEA AND SOCKS.

TAKE THAT, ROBERT FROST!

49

51

Maybelle's confirmation hearing as FIRST HOUND DOG:

DO YOU HAVE FLEAS?

DO YOU HAVE TICKS?

DO YOU DRINK FROM TOILETS?

HAVE A CARE, SIR! WITH THESE KINDS OF QUESTIONS, IT'S NO WONDER OUR BEST BREEDS ARE LOATHE TO ENTER PUBLIC SERVICE.

The world watches as WILL B. DUNN SKILLFULLY GUIDES MAYBELLE THROUGH HER CONFIRMATION:

DID YOU OR DID YOU NOT HIRE A MEXICAN CHIHUAHUA TO NANNY YOUR PUPPIES?!... JUST ANSWER THE QUESTION!

SUFFICE IT TO SAY, SENATOR, THIS PROUD CANINE RAISED HER OWN PUPPIES—AS UNFASHIONABLE AS THAT MIGHT BE TODAY—WHILE BRAVELY HOLDING DOWN A FULL-TIME POSITION AS A FIRST-RATE HUNTING DOG...

...NOT TO MENTION HER AWESOME RESPONSIBILITIES JUST LOLLYGAGGING AROUND DUB'S SERVICE STATION...

...SHE DOESN'T DRINK FROM TOILETS, DROOL ON STRANGERS, OR HAVE DOG BREATH, LIKE CERTAIN SENATORS I COULD MENTION!...

OUCH!

WILL B. DUNN BRILLIANTLY DEFENDS MAYBELLE'S NOMINATION:

NOW FRIENDS, I KNOW THERE ARE THOSE WHO WOULD SAY MAYBELLE...

...AIN'T NOTHIN' BUT A HOUND DOG...

CRYIN' ALL THE TIME...

...SHE AIN'T NEVER CAUGHT A RABBIT...

...AND SHE AIN'T NO FRIEND OF MINE!

WELL, I SAY, "BULL HOCKEY!"

I HOPE BILL IS WATCHING!

WE HAVE REASON TO BELIEVE YOU HAVE A FLEA AND TICK PROBLEM!

WHO, ME?!

THE DOG.

SAYS WHO?

THERE ARE WHITE HOUSE LEAKS.

LEAKS?!

LEAKS?

BULL HOCKEY! MAYBELLE IS COMPLETELY HOUSEBROKE!

Row 1:

BYPASS CELEBRATES AS MAYBELLE SAILS THROUGH HER CONFIRMATION FOR FIRST HOUND DOG:

MAYBELLE'S GONNA FOLLOW IN MILLIE'S PAW TRACKS!

THANKS TO WILL B. DUNN!

JUST THINK— THE PRESIDENT'S HOUND DOG ONCE DROOLED ON ME!

WILL B. DUNN IS GONNA HAVE CONGRESSIONAL PRAYER BREAKFASTS OUT THE WAZOO AFTER THIS!

—BUT NOT EVERYONE REJOICES!

THE OFFICE OF BYPASS HIGH GUIDANCE COUNSELOR NATHAN GOODVIBES:

I SHOULD'VE BEEN TAPPED FOR SECRETARY OF FEELINGS!

Row 2:

MR. GOODVIBES BROODS OVER THE IMMINENT CONFIRMATION OF MAYBELLE AS FIRST HOUND DOG:

I, NATHAN GOODVIBES, MEN'S MOVEMENT GURU, ACE FACILITATOR, AND RENOWNED ADVICE COLUMNIST FOR MODERN DEPRESSION...

...WAS PASSED OVER FOR SECRETARY OF FEELINGS...

...WHILE THIS... THIS...THIS MANGY CUR WILL SIT IN THE LAP OF POWER!...

I JUST DON'T GET IT!

THE PRESIDENT SEEMS SO SENSITIVE TO THE FEELINGS OF WOMEN, GAYS AND MINORITIES—

WHY ISN'T HE SENSITIVE TO MINE?

Row 3:

MR. GOODVIBES GETS IN TOUCH WITH HIS FEELINGS ABOUT BEING PASSED OVER:

THE PRESIDENT SEEMS SO SUPPORTIVE OF WOMEN, GAYS, HISPANICS, THE ELDERLY AND HANDICAPPED—WHY ISN'T HE SUPPORTIVE OF ME?!!

INSTEAD OF MAYBELLE!

THIS IS MAKING ME FEEL BAD ABOUT MYSELF!

THE CHILD IN ME IS FEELING VERY ABANDONED RIGHT NOW! I'M EXPERIENCING STRESSFUL FEELINGS... FEELINGS OF ENVY, LEFT-OUT-NESS, JEALOUSY...

...AND THE PARENT IN ME GIVES THE CHILD IN ME PERMISSION TO OWN THOSE FEELINGS!

I'M GONNA *GET* MAYBELLE!

Row 4:

PASSED OVER FOR SECRETARY OF FEELINGS, HUMAN RESOURCE GURU NATHAN GOODVIBES PLOTS TO GET MAYBELLE:

—BUT IN A NURTURING, SUPPORTIVE WAY!

YOU SUMMONED ME, MR. GOODVIBES?

AH, YES, IDA MAE!... AS AN ANIMAL RIGHTSER AND ALL-ROUND SENSITIVE PERSON, I GUESS YOU'RE PRETTY UPSET THESE DAYS!

NO MORE THAN USUAL, SIR.

OH? YOU'RE NOT UP-IN-ARMS OVER THE MAYBELLE NOMINATION?

SENSING HER CONSCIOUSNESS MAY BE INADEQUATELY RAISED ON THE TOPIC SHE SQUIRMS:

UH...WELL...I...UH CERTAINLY SUPPORT MAYBELLE'S ASPIRATIONS AS A CANINO-AMERICAN...

I SEE.

...GOODVIBES PLAYS HER LIKE A FIDDLE!

IDA MAE, I CAN'T BELIEVE A SENSITIVE PERSON LIKE YOU CAN STAND BY WHILE MAYBELLE GETS CONFIRMED!

WELL, I CERTAINLY SUPPORT HER ASPIRATIONS AS A CANINO-AMERICAN...

MAYBELLE'S ASPIRATIONS?!! WHAT ABOUT THE ASPIRATIONS OF THE COUNTLESS TINY INNOCENT CREATURES SHE HAS HELPED STALK AND DESTROY?!!

MARLETTE

THE HELPLESS QUAIL, POSSUM TURKEY AND DEER!...

I, FOR ONE, CERTAINLY WOULDN'T WANT THE BLOOD OF BAMBI ON MY HANDS!

B-B-BAMBI?

GOODVIBES CRAFTILY TRIGGERS IDA MAE'S GUILT GLAND!...

IDA MAE TESTIFIES AGAINST MAYBELLE...

THIS NOMINEE IS A NOTORIOUS STALKER OF INNOCENT WILDLIFE!

MAYBELLE HAS AIDED AND ABETTED DUB DUBOSE IN THE SLAUGHTER OF QUAIL, POSSUM, RACCOON AND DEER...

MARLETTE

SHE HAS BEEN TOTALLY INSENSITIVE TO THEIR PERSONHOOD AS ANIMALS!

BULL HOCKEY!

ARE YOU SAYING MAYBELLE BEHAVED LIKE AN ANIMAL?

IT'S INHUMAN!

...AND FURTHERMORE, MAYBELLE'S ATTITUDE TOWARD CATS IS APPALLING!... SHE'S OUT OF ANOTHER CENTURY!...

SHE HAS BELONGED TO ALL-CANINE KENNEL CLUBS... SHE HAS SNICKERED AT DEAD CAT JOKES!...

MARLETTE

SHE HAS EVEN CHASED CATS!

IS THIS THE MESSAGE WE WANT TO SEND TODAY? THAT CAT BASHING IS OKAY?!!

MEOW!

CELEBRITY CATS TESTIFY AGAINST MAYBELLE!

SHE'S DETHPICABLE!

MERCHANDISING CATS...

SHE'S FAT AND LAZY AND PROUD OF IT!

MARLETTE

MOVIE CATS...

MEOW!

...AND EVEN THE WHITE HOUSE CAT!

THANK YOU FOR GRANTING US AN AUDIENCE, YOUR SOCKSNESS!

WE'RE TOAST!

GRRRRRRRRR

LOOK — THE FIRST FELINE, SOCKS THE CAT, IS TESTIFYING AGAINST MAYBELLE!

MEOW!

MEOW! MEOW! MEOW!

MEOW! MEOW! MEOW! MEOW!

WOOF!

UH-OH!

MEOW! MEOW! MEOW!

WOOF! WOOF! WOOF!

IT'S TURNING UGLY!

Bypass Bugle

SOCKS BLASTS FIRST HOUND NOMINEE

THE FIRST FELINE TESTIFIED TODAY THAT MAYBELLE IS A KNOWN CAT BASHER!...

...AND SOCKS HERSELF WOULD NOT FEEL SAFE WITH MAYBELLE ON THE PREMISES!

APPARENTLY, THE WHITE HOUSE ISN'T BIG ENOUGH FOR THEM BOTH.

THAT'S OKAY — MAYBELLE'S A YARD DOG!

MR. PRESIDENT, ISN'T IT TRUE THAT MRS. CLINTON SUPPORTS SOCKS AND HAS ALWAYS OPPOSED A DOG IN THE WHITE HOUSE?

...AND THAT THE FIRST HOUND DOG WAS YOUR IDEA? ...AND NOW YOU HAVE TO BAG IT BECAUSE HILLARY DISAPPROVES?!

NOW WAIT JUST A DARN MINUTE!

ARE YOU SUGGESTING I DON'T WEAR THE PANTYHOSE IN THIS FAMILY?!

UNDER SIEGE BY HIS OWN CAT FOR HIS NOMINATION OF MAYBELLE FOR FIRST HOUND DOG, THE PRESIDENT IS ON THE DEFENSIVE:

NO COMMENT.

MR. PRESIDENT, DOES SOCKS REPRESENT YOUR VIEWS ON YOUR NOMINEE?

NO COMMENT.

DID YOU KNOW MAYBELLE WAS A CAT BASHER WHEN YOU NOMINATED HER?

NO COMMENT.

IF YOU CAN'T CONTROL YOUR OWN CAT, HOW DO YOU EXPECT TO CONTROL CONGRESS?

HILLARY!

BOY, THAT REALLY TICKED ME OFF!

HOLY ROLLERS

I GOT CALLED FOR A TECHNICAL FOUL IN *CHURCH LEAGUE BASKETBALL!*

— FOR SPEAKING IN TONGUES TO THE REFEREE!

NEXT WEEK, WE PLAY *FIRST BAPTIST OF RALEIGH* IN CHURCH LEAGUE BASKETBALL!

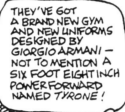

THEY'VE GOT A BRAND NEW GYM AND NEW UNIFORMS DESIGNED BY GIORGIO ARMANI — NOT TO MENTION A SIX FOOT EIGHT INCH POWER FORWARD NAMED TYRONE!

...BUT WHAT WE LACK IN HEIGHT, TALENT AND EXPERIENCE, WE MAKE UP FOR IN *HEART!*

WE'RE DOG MEAT!

FIRST CHURCH IN RALEIGH WILL TRY TO INTIMIDATE US WITH THEIR FLASHY ARMANI GAME UNIFORMS...

...THEIR ROMAN NUMERAL GAME CLOCK...

...AND THEIR STAINED-GLASS BACKBOARDS!

IF MY CHURCH LEAGUE BASKETBALL TEAM IS GOING TO ADVANCE IN THE TOURNAMENT...

...WE'VE GOT TO WORK ON THE FUNDAMENTALS...

HOLY ROLLERS

...LIKE SHOWING UP FOR THE GAME!

PREACHER, WHAT HAPPENED TO YOU?

IT'S THE PRICE I PAY FOR COACHING MY TEAM TO VICTORY IN THE *CHURCH LEAGUE BASKETBALL TOURNAMENT!*

THEY BAPTIZED ME IN GATORADE!

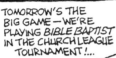

TOMORROW'S THE BIG GAME—WE'RE PLAYING *BIBLE BAPTIST* IN THE CHURCH LEAGUE TOURNAMENT!...

THEY'RE HEAVILY FAVORED, BUT I REALLY BELIEVE IF WE GET OUT THERE AND PLAY HARD, HANG TOUGH ON DEFENSE AND HIT THE OPEN SHOT, WE CAN WIN!

PREACHER, SOMETHING'S WRONG — MY BALL WON'T DRIBBLE!

WE'RE TOAST!

SEE.

A GOOD PLAYER-COACH KNOWS HOW TO HANDLE HOSTILE CROWDS ON THE ROAD...

BOOO ROLLERS   BOO

I TRY TO NEUTRALIZE THEIR *HOME COURT* ADVANTAGE...

...BY USING MY UNIQUE GIFTS AS A MAN OF GOD TO TAKE THE CROWD OUT OF THE GAME!...

THEY HATE IT WHEN I *PART* THEIR *WAVE!*

SORRY I MISSED THE SHOT THAT LOST THE TOURNAMENT FOR US, PREACHER!...

...BUT *HEY*— WAIT'LL *NEXT* YEAR, *RIGHT?!*... HEH-HEH-HEH!...

NO, ACTUALLY...

...I THINK I'LL STRANGLE YOU RIGHT NOW!

61

Dear Mr. Goodvibes,
I am, like, chronically spacy, flaky and gullible...

Can you tell just by my symptoms, like, what my emotional state is?
Wow

Dear Wow,
California.

Dear Mr. Goodvibes,
As a therapist-advice columnist, is it possible you are totally screwed-up...

...and are simply trying to work through your own emotional problems on your patients and readers instead of looking at yourself?
Wondering

Dear Wondering,
No.

Dear Mr. Goodvibes,
My inner child seems to be missing.

What can I do?
Distraught

Dear Distraught,
Check for its picture on your inner milk carton.

Dear Mr. Goodvibes,
My Inner Child is contemplating suing my Inner Parent.

Any comment?
Attorney-At-Law

Dear Attorney-At-Law,
Impossible -- Lawyers don't have an Inner Child!

Kudzu by Doug Marlette

HOLY CATFISH!

Dear Preacher,
    Please tell everybody that I'm dead!...Dead as a doornail!...

I keep reading my name in the papers as if I'm still alive and frankly it makes me sick!

Also, I realize imitation is the sincerest form of flattery, but I personally find it annoying. Please tell the impersonators to knock it off!...

MARLETTE

Please ask your readers to stop exploiting the dead or patronizing those who do...

I appreciate it very much.
            Elvis, (from beyond)

Dear Readers,
    For a scrap of this authentic Elvis missive send a check or money order for $10.00°° to Will B. Dunn % this paper.

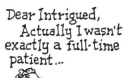

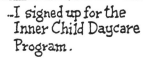

Dear Mr. Goodvibes, I am very proud of my parenting skills...

...Unfortunately, they are no match for my child's...

...Spoiled-Bratting Skills!

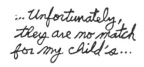

Dear Mr. Goodvibes, I am a therapist with exceptional *people skills*...

...but I always have problems with my patients who are agents or lawyers. Any suggestions?
Thwarted

Dear Thwarted, Work on your *reptile skills*.

HELLO?!... HUH? YEAH, THIS IS REVEREND DUNN!... ≴YAWN≴ WHAT TIME IS IT?!... TWO A.M.?!

OKAY!...OKAY! I'LL BE THERE!... WHERE ARE YOU?... YEAH!...YEAH!... OLD EIGHTY-SIX AND NEW HOPE ROAD... GIMME TEN MINUTES!...

≴GROAN≴ ONE OF THE PERKS OF MY CALLING!...

I'M ON TWENTY-FOUR HOUR CALL TO ADMINISTER LAST RITES FOR ROADKILL!

I DON'T MIND ADMINISTERING THE LAST RITES FOR ROADKILL...

I DON'T MIND THE WEIRD HOURS...

...OR GIVING THE EULOGIES!...

IT'S THE *PALL BEARING* THAT GETS ME!

SCRAPE SCRAPE SCRAPE

PREACHER, I HOPE YOU DON'T TAKE IT PERSONALLY THAT I'M PLAYING FOR MR. GOODVIBES AND THE SECULAR HUMANISTS IN THE INTERFAITH LEAGUE...

NO OFFENSE, BUT IT'S JUST THAT MR. GOODVIBES IS MORE SENSITIVE TO MY PERSONHOOD NEEDS AND CONFLICTS.

HE UNDERSTANDS THE TEAM PLAYER IN ME DOESN'T CARE ABOUT SCORING AND IS SATISFIED TO PLAY A LIMITED ROLE TO HELP THE TEAM WIN...

...YET MY INNER POWER FORWARD WANTS TO TAKE IT TO THE HOOP!

HE'S SENSITIVE ALL RIGHT!

IDA MAE, WHY DID YOU CALL TIME-OUT? I CALLED FOR A FULL COURT DRESS!

PRESS?

I THOUGHT YOU SAID "STRESS"! FULL-COURT STRESS!

I CALLED TIME-OUT BECAUSE I FELT THE NEED FOR STRESS MANAGEMENT COUNSELING!

I LOVE PLAYING THE SECULAR HUMANISTS!

MR. GOODVIBES, I NOTICE YOU HAVE A TENDENCY TO GIVE MORE PLAYING TIME TO THE TALLER PLAYERS...

AREN'T YOU DISCRIMINATING AGAINST THE LESS ALTITUDINALLY ADVANTAGED...

I HEAR YOU, IDA MAE, AND THE SENSITIVE, SUPPORTIVE CARE GIVER IN ME SHARES YOUR CONCERN...

...BUT THE BOBBY KNIGHT IN ME SAYS, "SHUT UP AND SIT DOWN!"

Dear Mr. Goodvibes, I asked my therapist if I could call him by his first name...

...to ease the formality and establish a rapport.

He said, "By all means!" So I asked him his first name...

He said, "Doctor."

68

HOW DID I GET MYSELF INTO DOING THESE *ROADKILL FUNERALS*?!

I MEAN, WHAT CAN YOU SAY IN THE *EULOGY*?

MARLETTE

HE LIVED LIFE IN THE *FAST LANE*!

PREACHER, YOU MADE THE COVER OF "STEEPLE MAGAZINE"!

I DID?!

CONGRATULATIONS!

OH, NO!

WHAT'S WRONG, PREACHER? I THOUGHT YOU'D BE *PLEASED*!

HOLY CATFISH!

steeple

ROADKILL RECTOR

HOLY CATFISH! I FINALLY MAKE THE COVER OF "STEEPLE" AND FOR WHAT!?!

"WILL B. DUNN: THE ROADKILL RECTOR"!

WITH ALL MY SERVICE TO HUMANITY, *THIS* IS WHAT I'M RECOGNIZED FOR! HOW HUMILIATING!

MARLETTE

APPARENTLY, LAST RITES FOR ROADKILL IS ON THE CUTTING EDGE OF PASTORAL CARE! YOU'RE A PIONEER! THE ANIMAL RIGHTS FOLKS WANT TO CANONIZE YOU!

DID YOU READ THE PROFILE? THEY CALL YOU THE "ASPHALT ANGEL"... THE "SAMARITAN OF CEMENT"... THE "PARSON OF POSSUM"!

"REVEREND OF REVOLTING"!

LISTEN TO THIS! THEY CALL ME "MASTER OF THE CEMENT LAMENT"!... HOLY CATFISH!

COULD BE WORSE.

WHAT COULD BE WORSE THAN BEING LABELED "*THE RECTOR OF ROADKILL*" IN A NATIONAL MAGAZINE?!

MARLETTE

"SHAMAN OF SQUISH"!... "MINISTER OF MUSH!"... "BROWN STAIN BRAHMIN"!...

OKAY!... OKAY!

"PASTOR OF PAVEMENT PUTRESCENCE"!...

STEEPLE MAGAZINE PEGGED ME AS THE "ROADKILL RECTOR"— NOW I'LL NEVER LIVE THAT DOWN! I'LL BE THE LAUGHING-STOCK OF THE PASTOR'S CONFERENCE!

...AND WHY?! ALL BECAUSE I HAD THE DECENCY TO SAY LAST RITES OVER POOR DEAD CRITTERS WHEN NOBODY ELSE WILL! WHY, WHY, WHY DID I DO IT? WHY DIDN'T I JUST STAY HOME IN BED?!

MARLETTE

I THOUGHT IT WAS BECAUSE THE DEPT. OF TRANSPORTATION PAID YOU TWENTY FIVE BUCKS A POP!

OH, SHUT UP!

Dear Mr. Goodvibes,
I am always down and never up...

Am I a manic-depressive personality?
Blue

Dear Blue,
It don't mean a thing if it ain't got that mood-swing.

MARLETTE

PREACHER, WE MAY NOT HAVE WON THE INTER-FAITH HOOPS TOURNAMENT...

MARLETTE

...BUT OUR TEAM WAS VOTED "MOST HUMBLE" BY THE MEDIA...

SWELL.

OF COURSE, WE HAD A LOT TO BE HUMBLE ABOUT!

THOMAS WOLFE WAS RIGHT:

YOU CAN'T GO HOME AGAIN!

≠SIGH≠

I TAKE IT YOUR PARENTS CHANGED THE LOCKS ON THE DOORS AGAIN!

MARLETTE

IS THAT ALL THERE IS, PREACHER?

THAT'S A YOUNG MAN'S QUESTION, BOY... "IS THAT ALL THERE IS?!"

AT MY AGE...

I CERTAINLY HOPE SO.

IF HE SEES *SHAQUILLE O'NEAL'S* SHADOW, IT MEANS SIX MORE WEEKS OF *NBA PLAYOFFS!*

DING-DING!

UH-OH! IT'S THE SCHOOL BULLY, *BOOGER BRYANT,* PULLING UP FOR GAS WITH HIS GIRLFRIEND *LORETTA!*

FILL 'ER UP, DUBOSE!

YES, BOOGER!

HEY, KUDZU!

ER- HEY, LORETTA!

DUBOSE, WERE YOU FLIRTING WITH MY WOMAN?!

I HATE THESE PSYCHODRAMAS!

I ASKED YOU A QUESTION, DUBOSE— WERE YOU FLIRTING WITH MY WOMAN?!

NO WAY, BOOGER! NUH-UH! NOT ME! EVERYBODY KNOWS SHE BELONGS TO YOU! NOSIREE! NOT ME!

I WOULD NEVER IN A MILLION YEARS FLIRT WITH *LORETTA!*

WHASSAMATTER, DUBOSE? LORETTA AIN'T GOOD *ENOUGH* FOR YOU?!

71

Panel 1: OH, KUDZU — I'M HAVING PROBLEMS WITH MY ENGLISH HOMEWORK!... WOULD YOU COME OVER TONIGHT AND HELP ME OUT?!

Panel 2: ARE YOU NUTS, LORETTA?! YOUR BOYFRIEND BOOGER WOULD *KILL* ME.

Panel 3: BUT YOU'RE SO SMART AND I HAVE SO MUCH TROUBLE WITH THOSE NOUNS AND VERBS AND *PROPOSITIONS*!...

Panel 4: *PREPOSITIONS!* SEE.

Panel 5: NASAL, I'M MAKING OUT MY WILL AND IF ANYTHING SHOULD HAPPEN TO ME I WANT YOU TO HAVE YOUR PICK OF MY CD COLLECTION!

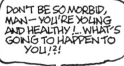

Panel 6: DON'T BE SO MORBID, MAN— YOU'RE YOUNG AND HEALTHY!... WHAT'S GOING TO HAPPEN TO YOU?!

Panel 7: I'M GOING TO HELP BOOGER BRYANT'S GIRLFRIEND WITH HER HOMEWORK!

Panel 8: CAN I HAVE YOUR *R.E.M.* AND *PEARL JAM?*

Panel 9: I'M DEAD, PREACHER! BOOGER'S GONNA KILL ME!

NOW DON'T GET PANICKY, BOY!...

Panel 10: WHY DON'T YOU JUST GO TO BOOGER, EXPLAIN THE SITUATION, TELL HIM HOW HIS GIRL SEEMS TO BE INFATUATED WITH YOU, AND JUST SETTLE IT BETWEEN YOU LIKE REASONABLE YOUNG MEN!

Panel 11: I THINK I JUST FELT MY AUTHORITY ERODE!

Panel 12: PREACHER, WHEN I GO I WANT YOU TO DO THE *EULOGY!*

FINE, BUT YOU'RE A LITTLE YOUNG TO WORRY ABOUT THAT, AREN'T YOU?

Panel 13: BOOGER BRYANT'S GIRLFRIEND LORETTA HAS THE HOTS FOR ME!

OH.

Panel 14: DO YOU WANT ME TO PICK THE MUSIC, TOO?

73

FRIENDS, LET US PRAY FOR SISTER POTTS WHO JUST GOT OUT OF THE HOSPITAL...

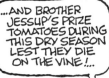
...AND BROTHER JESSUP'S PRIZE TOMATOES DURING THIS DRY SEASON LEST THEY DIE ON THE VINE!...

...AND ESPECIALLY *KUDZU DUBOSE* WHO IS DATING THE SCHOOL BULLY BOOGER BRYANT'S GIRL-FRIEND!

ARRRGH!

UH-OH! I MAY HAVE JUST BROKEN THE SEAL OF *CONFESSION!*

Dear Preacher,
Thank you for all you have done for our nation's roadkill.

Why can't everyone be as sensitive as you are to our furry friend fatalities?
Concerned

Dear Concerned,
Let's face it — one man's roadkill is another man's speed bump.

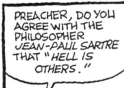
PREACHER, DO YOU AGREE WITH THE PHILOSOPHER JEAN-PAUL SARTRE THAT "HELL IS OTHERS."

OCCASIONALLY.

OCCASIONALLY? WHEN?!

RIGHT NOW.

THESE RELIGIOUS NUTS SURE GIVE THE REST OF US A BAD NAME!...

BUT, PREACHER...

...HOW DO YOU KNOW *YOU'RE* NOT A *NUT?!*

GOOD POINT.

THE ONLY WAY TO BE SURE YOU'RE NOT A NUT...

...IS TO KNOW HOW MUCH OF A *NUT* YOU ARE!

74

75

OUR TOWN COSMETIC SURGEON WAS A FINE MAN...

...A MAN WHO PREFERRED CASH UP FRONT FOR A FACE LIFT OR NOSE JOB...

...BUT IF YOU WERE A LITTLE STRAPPED FOR CASH WOULD LET YOU CHARGE IT ON VISA OR MASTERCARD!...

HE PUT THE *PLASTIC* IN *PLASTIC* SURGERY!

DEAR PREACHER, I AM A RUGGED, EX-MARINE JOHN WAYNE-TYPE...

...WHO IS SERIOUSLY CONSIDERING A SEX-CHANGE OPERATION. ANY ADVICE?
MACHO

Dear Macho,
A man's gotta do what a man's gotta do!

Dear Preacher,
I attended a "Roadkill" funeral of yours recently...

...in which you referred to the deceased as a "pavement pancake"!

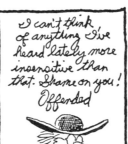

I can't think of anything I've heard lately more insensitive than that. Shame on you!
Offended

Dear Offended,
Try "Highway Hash"!

BROTHER HARPER RAN OFF WITH HIS CHURCH SECRETARY!... TSK-TSK!... SCANDALOUS!

THERE BUT FOR THE GRACE OF GOD GO I!...

THAT'S WHY I HAVE A POLICY OF HIRING ONLY SECRETARIES WHO ARE FACIALLY CHALLENGED!

FACIALLY CHALLENGED?

UGLIER'N A MUD FENCE!

Panel 1: LOOK, KUDZU — THE *BYPASS HIGH ANNUAL* (OF WHICH I AM EDITOR) JUST CAME OUT *HOT OFF THE PRESS!*

I'M VERY HAPPY FOR YOU, IDA MAE.

Panel 2: KUDZU, IT'S THE OFFICIAL HISTORY OF THE YEAR IN PICTURES — AREN'T YOU EXCITED?!

BIG DEAL!

Panel 3: IT'S OUR CLASS RECORD — ONE OF THE MOST IMPORTANT DOCUMENTS OF OUR YOUNG LIVES!...DON'T YOU WANT TO SEE EVERYBODY'S PICTURES?!

NOT REALLY.

Panel 4: YOU WERE ABSENT ON PICTURE DAY, RIGHT?

SO WHAT?

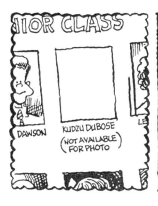

Panel 5: IOR CLASS

DAWSON

KUDZU DUBOSE (NOT AVAILABLE FOR PHOTO)

LE

Panel 6: GEE, KUDZU, I CAN'T BELIEVE YOU WERE ABSENT ON *PICTURE DAY* FOR THE SCHOOL YEARBOOK, THE ARCHIVAL RECORD OF OUR PASSAGE THROUGH THESE HALLOWED HALLS, PERHAPS THE MOST IMPORTANT DOCUMENT OF OUR YOUNG LIVES!

Panel 7: IN YEARS TO COME, PEOPLE WILL LOOK BACK AND SEE EVERYBODY BUT YOU!... VERANDA, MAURICE, NASAL, MR. GOODVIBES... BUT NO KUDZU!

Panel 8: HEY — I'LL SURVIVE!

SURVIVE?! ACCORDING TO THIS, YOU DON'T EXIST!

Panel 9: SO WHAT IF I WAS LEFT OUT OF THE CLASS MUG SHOTS IN THE YEARBOOK — SURELY I SHOW UP ELSEWHERE IN THE CANDID GROUP PHOTOS...

Panel 10: NO, ACTUALLY, KUDZU... YOU WERE IN SEVERAL SHOTS WE USED ORIGINALLY...

Panel 11: ...BUT I EXERCISED MY EDITOR'S PREROGATIVE TO HAVE YOU AIRBRUSHED OUT!

Panel 12: YOU *WHAT!?*

CONSISTENCY, KUDZU — WE DIDN'T WANT TO CONFUSE OUR READERS — AFTER ALL, YOU WEREN'T IN THE MUG SHOTS!

Panel 13: WHAT'S WRONG, KUDZU!

I WAS OUT SICK THE DAY OUR PICTURES WERE TAKEN FOR THE YEARBOOK!

Panel 14: I'M MISSING FROM THE HIGH SCHOOL ANNUAL! IT'S LIKE I DON'T EXIST!... I'VE BEEN EXPUNGED FROM THE RECORD!

Panel 15: I'M A NON-PERSON! LIKE IN COMMUNIST RUSSIA — I'M LIKE *BREZHNEV!*

AW, C'MON!

Panel 16: NO, REALLY! EVERYBODY ELSE IS THERE! NASAL, VERANDA, IDA MAE,...

OOH! THERE'S *BREZHNEV!*

WELCOME TO THE *MARLA MAPLES* CHAPTER OF *FUTURE HOMEWRECKERS OF AMERICA...*

...Y'KNOW, SOME PEOPLE THINK THE TYPICAL *OTHER WOMAN* IS JUST AN AIRHEAD!

...BUT BELIEVE ME, IT TAKES A VERY STRONG MIND TO BE THE *OTHER WOMAN...*

... A VERY STRONG MIND SURROUNDED BY LOTS AND LOTS OF CURLY BLONDE HAIR!

TODAY AT THE *MARLA MAPLES* CHAPTER OF *FUTURE HOMEWRECKERS* WE'RE GOING TO DISCUSS THE *TRUMP DIVORCE!...*

PRE-NUPTIAL CONTRACTS, POST-NUPTIAL AMENDMENTS, SUITS, COUNTER-SUITS, COMMUNITY PROPERTY, CAPITAL GAINS TAX AND ESTATE LAW!

...AND THEY CALL US AIRHEADS!

PREACHER, SOMETIMES I FEEL SO SILLY... LIKE AN OBJECT OF RIDICULE...

...LIKE I'M SOME CARTOON CHARACTER WHOSE EVERY SYLLABLE DESERVES TO BE ENCIRCLED BY A COMIC STRIP BALLOON!

I GUESS WE ALL FEEL THAT WAY SOMETIMES, *RIGHT,* PREACHER? HEH-HEH!

NOT REALLY.

...AND DO YOU, BILL, PROMISE TO LOVE, HONOR AND CHERISH MARY...

...AND PROMISE NOT TO TAKE ANY PROBLEMS ONTO TALK SHOWS FOR AT LEAST A YEAR PURSUANT TO THE BREAK-UP OF SAID MARRIAGE?...

HE DOES.

I HATE WHEN THEIR LAWYERS ARE ASKED TO DRAW UP THE VOWS!

THAT WAS THE ROWDIEST BUNCH OF *PALL BEARERS* I EVER SAW !...

WE NEVER SHOULD'VE LET THEM DRIVE THE *HEARSE!*

AFTER THE SERVICE, THEY ALL MADE A MAD DASH FOR IT YELLING "*SHOTGUN*"!

I WANT TO APOLOGIZE FOR MY *PALL BEARERS* I SELECTED...

COME ON— YOU'RE NOT GOING TO GIVE ME THE SILENT *TREATMENT*, ARE YOU?

I'VE NEVER HAD TO STAMP MY CASKETS "*THIS END UP*" BEFORE !

THAT'S THE LAST TIME I LET THAT BUNCH OF PALL BEARERS DRIVE THE HEARSE !...

WHAT HAPPENED? IT WAS A MESS!

ONE OF 'EM HAD TO HAVE AN *ESKIMO PIE* ON THE WAY TO THE CEMETERY...

FUNERAL PROCESSION GRIDLOCK IN THE *DAIRY QUEEN* PARKING LOT!

IF ADULTS ARE SO CONCERNED ABOUT THE EROSION OF THEIR AUTHORITY WITH YOUNG PEOPLE...

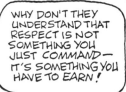
WHY DON'T THEY UNDERSTAND THAT RESPECT IS NOT SOMETHING YOU JUST *COMMAND*— IT'S SOMETHING YOU HAVE TO *EARN!*

AMEN!

AMEN, *SIR!*

79

NOW WHAT SEEMS TO BE THE PROBLEM?

MILY UNSELOR

KUDZU'S AT THAT AWKWARD AGE...

MARLETTE

...ALWAYS HAS BEEN.

B. DU..

FAMILY COUNSELOR

JIM IS ON MARRIAGE NUMBER THREE AND LOUISE IS ON MARRIAGE NUMBER FOUR!...

SERIAL MARRIAGES ARE BECOMING THE NORM!

SURREAL MARRIAGES?

MARLETTE

THAT'S WHAT I SAID!

MY FAVORITE FLICK...

THE POIGNANT TALE OF A FLOCK OF DISENFRANCHISED YOUNG PARAKEETS...

MARLETTE

...AND THE RUN-DOWN PERCH AND PET SHOP THEY CALL HOME!

'KEETZ 'N' THE 'HOOD!

I FORESEE A BITTER CUSTODY BATTLE!

MARRIAGE COUNSELOR

—BUT THEY HAVE NO CHILDREN!

MARLETTE

OVER THE TV REMOTE CONTROL!

MARRIAGE COUNSELOR

THAT WAS THE WORST BUNCH OF PALLBEARERS I'VE EVER SEEN!

I'LL SAY.

THAT'S WHAT YOU GET WHEN YOU GO TO THE YELLOW PAGES UNDER RENT-A-PALL-BEARER!

I DID NOT! I FOUND THESE GUYS RIGHT OUTSIDE YOUR FUNERAL HOME!

THEY WERE HOLDING SIGNS THAT SAID: "WILL PALL BEAR FOR FOOD"!

I CAN'T BELIEVE MY PALLBEARERS DROPPED THE CASKET!

YOU CAN'T BLAME THEM COMPLETELY! AFTER ALL, IT WAS ICY AND SLIPPERY AFTER THAT SNOW.

STILL, AND ALL...

THEY DIDN'T HAVE TO USE THE COFFIN AS A BOBSLED!

Dear Mr. Goodvibes,
I met a woman in my group therapy who is absolutely gorgeous...

She has the most beautiful face and body I have ever seen but is a neurotic mess.

What should I do? Smitten

Dear Smitten,
Put a bag over her personality.

A GREATER ATTENTION SPAN, LORD...

...GRANT MY CONGREGATION A GREATER...

SAY, ISN'T IT TIME FOR A CURRENT AFFAIR?

THESE RIVAL TV PREACHERS REALLY STEAM ME!

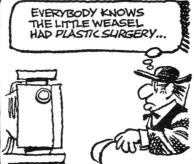

EVERYBODY KNOWS THE LITTLE WEASEL HAD *PLASTIC SURGERY*...

...BUT HE'S CLAIMING THE LORD HEALED HIS NOSE!

Dear Preacher, I am planning to have an Inner-Child transplant...

I have found a donor who is a fun-loving, life-affirming human being...

I, on the other hand, am a lawyer. What is the downside? Attorney-at-Law

Dear Attorney, The Inner Child may reject you.

‡SIGH‡ LIFE IS FULL OF AMBIGUITY!...

RIGHT, PREACHER?

YES AND NO.

WHEN YOU'RE A CHILD, LIFE IS IN SLO-MO...

WHEN YOU'RE AN ADULT, LIFE IS IN PLAY...

...AS YOU GROW OLDER, IT FEELS LIKE FAST FORWARD...

WHEN YOU HIT MID-LIFE, YOU TRY TO REWIND!

83

Kudzu by Doug Marlette

HMMPH!

BOY, THAT REALLY TICKS ME OFF!

THE NERVE OF THAT BLUE JAY OUTSIDE MY WINDOW THIS MORNING!...

...CALLING ME "CHOCOLATE GUT"!...

I DON'T HAVE A CHOCOLATE GUT!...

Marlette

...MY MUSCLES JUST MIGRATED SOUTH FOR THE WINTER!

OKAY, WHEN YOU'RE A CHILD, LIFE IS IN SLO-MO...

...AS AN ADULT, LIFE IS IN PLAY...

...AS YOU GROW OLDER, IT FEELS LIKE FAST FORWARD...

I LIKE YOUR ANALOGY, BUT WHAT ABOUT DEATH?

THE QUESTION IS WHETHER YOU'VE HIT STOP OR PAUSE!

I FIND IF I LET MEMBERS OF MY FLOCK COME UP HERE AND SING "HOW GREAT THOU ART"...

...WITH THE MORMON TABERNACLE CHOIR AND LONDON SYMPHONY ORCHESTRA AS BACK-UP...

...ATTENDANCE SOARS.

GOD BLESS KARAOKE!

...WITH THIS RING I THEE WED!

...THAT'S ALL WELL AND GOOD...

...BUT LET'S SEE YOU HAND OVER THE TV REMOTE CONTROL!

MINNIE RAN OFF WITH HER COMPUTER MOUSE!

COUNSELOR

85

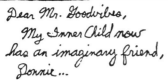

Dear Mr. Goodvibes,
My Inner Child now has an imaginary friend, Donnie...

Is this normal or what?
Anxious

Dear Anxious,
No. That's why you're asking an imaginary therapist.

Dear Mr. Goodvibes,
I am furious with my therapist, so I am writing you. He knows I don't drive...

...and at the end of my sessions he refuses to call me a taxi.
Steamed

Dear Steamed,
Okay. You're a taxi.

I JUST SAW "JURASSIC PARK" FOR THE *THIRD* TIME!

SPIELBERG IS A GENIUS!

YEAH...

...HIS HUMAN BEINGS ARE ALMOST *LIFE-LIKE*!

Dear Preacher,
You baptized my husband, Ralph, but apparently something didn't take...

He's still a lazy, shiftless, no-good bum. Is it something in the water?
Disappointed

Dear Disappointed,
Sorry. I can vouch for the baptismal pool...

...but there's nothing I can do for the gene pool.

86

TEE VEE JEEBIES!

WELCOME ONCE AGAIN TO AMERICA'S FAVORITE GAME SHOW: "WHAT'S MY TRAUMA?"...

LET'S WELCOME OUR CELEBRITY BASKET CASE TODAY, BROODING YOUNG ACTOR, MICKEY RORSHACH!...

...AND NOW OUR STAFF PSYCHIATRIST, DOCTOR OTTO SCHNELL, WILL LET OUR STUDIO AUDIENCE AND OUR VIEWERS AT HOME IN ON MICKEY'S SECRET EMOTIONAL SETBACK:

MICKEY RORSHACH, DIAGNOSED AS A SEVERE NARCISSISTIC PERSONALITY DISORDER WAS IGNORED AS A CHILD BY A DEPRESSED, SELF-ABSORBED MOTHER AND AN ALCOHOLIC FATHER...

OKAY PANEL, FIRE AWAY:

MICKEY, IS YOUR TRAUMA RELATED TO YOUR EXTREME SHORTNESS?

BOP!

NOW MICKEY, YOU PROMISED—NO HITTING! THAT'S TEN DOLLARS DOWN... JAN MURRAY:

MICKEY, WERE YOU PHYSICALLY ABUSED AS A CHILD?

Kudzu by Doug Marlette

>CLICK!<

WELCOME BACK TO "WHAT'S MY TRAUMA?" LET'S CONTINUE THE QUESTIONING OF TODAY'S CELEBRITY BASKET CASE, ACTOR MICKEY RORSHACH... PANEL?

MICKEY, YOU'RE WEARING SUNGLASSES INDOORS — WAS YOUR CHILDHOOD TRAUMA CONNECTED TO VISUAL IMPAIRMENT?... WERE YOU PARTIALLY BLINDED?

NO, I WAS NOT.

NICE TRY, JAN MURRAY — THAT'S FORTY DOLLARS DOWN — SUZANNE SOMERS?

YOUR FACIAL STUBBLE — DO YOU HAVE A FEAR OF RAZORS?

NO, I DO NOT.

I KNOW, I KNOW — WERE YOU ADDICTED TO DOWNERS?!

SORRY. NUH-UH.

SEXUALLY ABUSED AS A CHILD?!

THAT'S IT, PANEL!...WE'RE ALMOST OUT OF TIME!...AND YOU COULDN'T GUESS IT... MICKEY RORSHACH IS A **NARCISSISTIC PERSONALITY DISORDER**!

AAAWWW!...

I KNEW IT! THE SHADES WERE A DEAD GIVEAWAY!

...JOIN US NEXT WEEK WHEN ONCE AGAIN WE PLUMB THE DEPTHS ON "WHAT'S MY TRAUMA?" G'NIGHT, EVERYBODY!

EMPTEE VEE!

BACK-TO-BACK WHITE BOYS WAS BAD ENOUGH, BUT NOW: *THREEPEAT!*

WHOA! *NASAL T. LARDBOTTOM* VOTED "WHITEST WHITE BOY AT BYPASS HIGH" THREE YEARS IN A ROW! *HEAVY!*

HOW HUMILIATING! I'VE WORKED SO HARD AT MY *BROTHEROSITY!*

IT'S UNPRECEDENTED!

WHAT DOES IT TAKE TO BE ACCEPTED AS A *HOMEBOY?!*... I EVEN CHANGED MY NAME TO "NASAL X"!

LIFE IS UNFAIR!

Nasal is crushed!

I'VE DONE MY *DARNDEST* TO IMPROVE MY *BROTHER SKILLS!*... AND HOW AM I REWARDED?!...

BACK-TO-BACK WHITE BOYS WAS BURDEN ENOUGH, BUT THIS:

THREE-PEAT.

WHITEST WHITE BOY

WHAT DO THESE PEOPLE WANT?! I CHANGED MY NAME TO "NASAL X"... I'VE MASTERED INTRICATE HOMEBOY GREETINGS AND HANDSHAKES!... MY HIGH-FIVES ARE PERFECTION!

I SPEAK FLUENT JIVE! I MEAN, WHAT DO THESE DARNED PEOPLE WANT FROM ME?!

LOSE THE "DARNS"!

Devastated by the news of his selection as "whitest white boy" at Bypass High for an unprecedented third straight year, Nasal broods...

YO! THREEPEAT!

≠SIGH≠

I'VE LEFT NO STONE UNTURNED IN MY NEVER-ENDING QUEST FOR *BROTHEROSITY!* I DON'T GET IT!

I'M FLUENT IN JIVE! I'VE IMPROVED MY HANGTIME! MY HIGH-FIVES ARE FLAWLESS! YET I'M STILL BRANDED AS *LIGHTBREAD!*

I WONDER WHAT *MICHAEL JORDAN* WOULD DO IN A CASE LIKE...

BING!

EPIPHANY!

Thwarted in his quest for brotherosity, Nasal's three-peat selection as "whitest white boy" at Bypass High sparks another desperate bid for homeboyness:

BING!

HAVE YOU SEEN THE *WHITE BOY* LATELY?

NO, HE WAS PRETTY DOWN ABOUT WINNING THE *CAUCASIAN TRIPLE CROWN!*

WHAT IT BE, MY BROTHUHS!

NASAL!

CHROME-DOME MANIA!

92

93

KUDZU, I'M TOUCHED...

YOU KNOW I'VE TAKEN A LOT OF HEAT OVER MY DECISION TO SHAVE MY HEAD...

...AND IN A GESTURE OF FRIENDSHIP AND SOLIDARITY, YOU SHAVED YOUR *CHEST HAIR!*

NO, I DIDN'T!

OH... SORRY.

I WANT TO WRITE A NOVEL AS SIMPLE AND COMPELLING AS A TRADITIONAL FAIRY TALE...

...YET IN THE CONTEMPORY VOICE OF MY GENERATION!

Like, once upon a time...

DON'T HE LOOK NATURAL!

I COULDN'T BE HAPPIER!

A TISKET! A TASKET! A BRONZE GOLD-PLATED CASKET!

THERE'S SOMETHING UNSEEMLY ABOUT A GIDDY UNDERTAKER!

LORD, KEEP ME FROM JEALOUSY AND ENVY...

GRANT ME A GENEROUS, NON-COVETOUS NATURE...

...YOU KNOW — LIKE PREACHER GRAEBNER'S OVER AT ST. MATTHEWS...

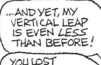

HEY, KUDZU, WHAT DO YOU SAY WE DRIVE UP TO MAKE-OUT POINT?!

UH...NOT TONIGHT, IDA MAE...I HAVE A HEADACHE!

YOU MEN ARE DISGUSTING! I SEE YOU DRESSING ME WITH YOUR EYES!...NOT TREATING ME LIKE AN OBJECT!...KEEPING YOUR HANDS TO YOURSELF!

IS THAT ALL YOU MEN THINK ABOUT: CONVERSATION, CONVERSATION, CONVERSATION?

WELL, I FOR ONE AM SICK OF BEING TREATED LIKE A WHOLE PERSON! I'M MORE THAN JUST A PAIR OF FRONTAL LOBES, Y'KNOW! I HAVE A BOD, TOO!

MARLETTE

SMACK!

I'M NOT READY FOR THE NINETIES!

SMITE THE UMPIRE!

FORGIVE HIM HIS TRESPASSES! LORD KNOWS I CAN'T!

HEAL HIS EYESIGHT, O LORD!

I LOVE CHURCH LEAGUE SOFTBALL!

OKAY, THIS IS CHURCH LEAGUE SOFTBALL!...

REMEMBER: WE'RE NOT JUST OUT HERE TO WIN — WE'RE OUT HERE TO HAVE FUN!

WHO SAYS WINNING ISN'T FUN?!

GOOD POINT.

OKAY, TEAM, GATHER AROUND THE PITCHER'S MOUND!

PREACHER'S GONNA GIVE US A PEP TALK!

I PREFER TO THINK OF IT AS THE SERMON ON THE MOUND!

SHAME ON YOU, NASAL!

I DON'T CARE IF THE CROWD WAS BOOING!...THIS IS CHURCH LEAGUE, FOR GOODNESS' SAKE!

YOU HAD NO BUSINESS MOONING THE STANDS!

YOU SAID TO TURN THE OTHER CHEEK!

LORD, YOU NEVER WRITE!... YOU NEVER CALL!...

OH, SURE, YOU CAN CALL MOSES, BUT DO I EVER HEAR FROM YOU?

MARLETTE

ZAP!

THE LORD DOESN'T RESPOND WELL TO GUILT-TRIPPING!

SCOUT'S HONOR? / HE'S DEAD, FOR CRYIN' OUT LOUD!

SORRY, BUT YOU HAVE NO IDEA HOW DISCONCERTING THOSE NEAR-DEATH EXPERIENCE FUNERALS CAN BE!

THE SO-CALLED DECEASED FLOATING OVER-HEAD LOOKING DOWN ON THE BODY!...

THE GREETING OF OLD FRIENDS AND FAMILY ON THE OTHER SIDE: "HI, MINNIE!" "YO, UNCLE LEW!"

MARLETTE

—AND THE LIGHT! IT'S ENOUGH TO BLIND SOMEBODY! WHO CAN CONCENTRATE ON A EULOGY!?!

THESE NEAR-DEATH EXPERIENCES ARE A BIG HEADACHE!

WHAT WITH THE SO-CALLED DECEASED FLOATING OVER-HEAD AND THE GREETING OF FAMILY AND OLD FRIENDS AND THE "EMBRACING-THE-LIGHT" THING...

...THEN THEY CHANGE THEIR MINDS AND DECIDE THEY HAVE UNFINISHED BUSINESS IN THIS LIFE!... WHO NEEDS IT!?!

MARLETTE

TRY COLLECTING YOUR FEES ON A NEAR-DEATH FUNERAL! / I KNOW— IT'S A NEAR-CASH EXPERIENCE!

I HATE THESE NEAR-DEATH EXPERIENCES!

MARLETTE

99

101

103

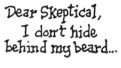

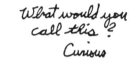

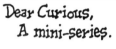

Dear Mr. Goodvibes,
I have been out of work for a long time and depressed and feeling worthless...

...when somebody sent me your advice column.

It restored my hope.

I figured if you could get a job, anybody could!

WELL, I'M VERY BUSY WITH MY GUIDANCE DUTIES HERE AT BYPASS HIGH...

...AND MY ADVICE COLUMN FOR MODERN DEPRESSION...

...THE CORPORATE STRESS MANAGEMENT SEMINARS AND WEEKEND DRUMMING RETREATS FOR SENSITIVE MALES...

I DON'T SEE HOW I COULD POSSIBLY— WHAT?!... LIZ AND LIZA ASKED FOR ME?!...

I SEE....THEY WANT ME TO SET UP A DAYCARE PROGRAM FOR CELEBRITY INNER CHILDREN!?!

HMMM... THIS MODERN TRANSLATION OF THE HOLY SCRIPTURES IS TROUBLING...

THEY'VE CHANGED ALL USES OF THE WORDS "WICKED," "EVIL" AND "SINFUL"...

...TO "MORALLY CHALLENGED"!

AND DO YOU, LANA, TAKE DWAYNE TO BE YOUR LAWFULLY WEDDED HUBBY?

HUSBAND!

SORRY, HUSBAND.

I'VE LEARNED TO TREAT THESE VOWS AS CASUALLY AS THE COUPLES DO!

NATHAN GOODVIBES, PhD.

THAT'S DOCTOR GOODVIBES.

...CRACK GUIDANCE COUNSELOR AT BYPASS HIGH...

POPULAR ADVICE COLUMNIST FOR *MODERN DEPRESSION* MAGAZINE...

Don't worry. Be happy.

GURU OF THE MEN'S MOVEMENT AND AUTHOR OF THE *SENSITIVE MALE'S BIBLE*:

IRON NATHAN by NATHAN GOODVIBES

...A SUCCESS BY ANY MEASURE, YET AT NIGHT, HIS SLUMBER IS HAUNTED BY A SINGLE RECURRING DREAM--

HELLO, NATHAN?... HILLARY!...WE'RE IN NEED OF SOME *FIRST FAMILY THERAPY!*

A RECURRING DREAM:

THANK YOU FOR COMING AT SUCH SHORT NOTICE, MR. GOODVIBES!

DOCTOR GOODVIBES!

IT'S ROGER, THE PRESIDENT'S BROTHER AGAIN! HE'S GRANTING UNAUTHORIZED INTERVIEWS...

AND BILL'S MOTHER— SHE CAN'T STAY AWAY FROM THE TRACK — I THINK SHE MAY HAVE A PROBLEM!

NOW, HILLARY— LET ME BE THE JUDGE OF THAT!

OH, DR. GOODVIBES! YOU'RE SO WISE AND CARING!

NATHAN GOODVIBES, PhD *FIRST FAMILY THERAPIST*

PREACHER, IF I ASK YOU A QUESTION YOU WON'T THINK I'M SILLY OR ANYTHING, WILL YOU?

OF COURSE NOT, KUDZU!

DO PARAKEETS HAVE SOULS?

GOOD QUESTION, BOY— I DON'T KNOW.

WHAT A *DWEEB!*

New Year's Resolutions

HMM...

⸮SIGH⸝

IT'S NOT EASY TO MAKE RESOLUTIONS WHEN YOU'RE ALREADY *PERFECT!*

107

MR. GOODVIBES HAS A RECURRING DREAM:

I CAME AS QUICKLY AS POSSIBLE, HILLARY!

OH, DOCTOR GOODVIBES, I'M WORRIED ABOUT CHELSEA — WE USED TO HAVE SUCH A GOOD MOTHER-DAUGHTER RAPPORT!..

NOW SHE SEEMS EMBARRASSED TO EVEN BE SEEN AROUND HER PARENTS!

NOW, HILLARY — THIS IS QUITE NORMAL IN YOUNG TEENS..

WE CALL IT THE "I-COULD-JUST-DIE!" STAGE...

OH, NATHAN, I KNEW YOU COULD SHED SOME INSIGHT! WON'T YOU STAY FOR A WHITE HOUSE DINNER?!

NATHAN GOODVIBES DREAMS OF BEING THE FIRST FAMILY THERAPIST:

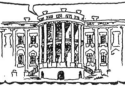

BILL, WHY DON'T YOU SHARE WITH THE GROUP HOW YOU TRULY FEEL ABOUT ROGER'S SHENANIGANS!..

FRANKLY, MR. GOODVIBES, I KNOW IT'S NOT EASY BEING FIRST BROTHER, AND I SUPPORT THE LITTLE GUY'S STRUGGLE...

TELL THE TRUTH, BILL!

BUTT OUT, HILLARY!

QUIET, BOTH OF YOU!.. NOW, ROGER, HOW DO YOU FEEL ABOUT WHAT BILL SAID?...

OH, MR. PERFECT?!.. MR. OVERACHIEVER?! WHAT ELSE COULD HE SAY?! HE'S SUCH A GOOD BOY IT MAKES YOU WANNA PUKE!

GOOD, ROGER! LET IT OUT! I'M HERE FOR YOU!

SHUT UP, BILL!

...AND I GUESS IT'S ALWAYS BEEN MY PARENTS' DREAM THAT I'D BE THE FIRST COLLEGE GRADUATE IN THE FAMILY!...

SPEAKING OF DREAMS, DID I EVER MENTION THIS RECURRING DREAM I HAVE ABOUT BEING THE FIRST FAMILY THERAPIST!...

IT'S THE CRAZIEST THING — HILLARY ALWAYS CALLS WITH SOME CRISIS AND —

TELEPHONE, MR. GOODVIBES!

IT'S THE WHITE HOUSE!

HOLD THAT THOUGHT!

MR. GOODVIBES GETS THE CALL!

YES, MRS. CLINTON!

YES, IT IS AN HONOR TO HEAR FROM YOU!...

HOW WOULD I FEEL ABOUT A CABINET POST?...

WELL, LET'S SEE NOW — MY INTERNAL PARENT IS QUIETLY PROUD TO BE ASKED AND IS WEIGHING THE RISKS AND BENEFITS OF PUBLIC SERVICE...

..WHILE MY INNER CHILD IS WETTING ITS PANTS!

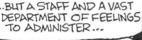

110

111

BUNS OF STEEL, LORD! GIVE ME BUNS OF STEEL!

KNOCK! KNOCK!

PREACHER, MAMA SENT OVER SOME OF HER HOMEMADE BISCUITS!

THE LORD WORKS IN MYSTERIOUS WAYS!

THEY MAKE IT SOUND SO EASY...

"JUST SAY 'NO'."

"JUST DO IT."

NEVER TRUST A CULTURE WHOSE COMMANDMENTS START WITH THE WORD "JUST".

LIFE IS UNFAIR!

NOBODY SAID IT WOULD BE FAIR!

LIFE IS HARD!

NOBODY SAID IT WOULD BE EASY!

LIFE IS COMPLICATED!

NOBODY SAID IT WOULD BE SIMPLE!

NOBODY SAID ANYTHING!

NOBODY SAID THEY WOULD!

KUDZU, IT SOUNDS TO ME LIKE YOU'RE HAVING A MID-LIFE CRISIS!

AT SEVENTEEN?

YOU ALWAYS WERE PRECOCIOUS!

115

HOLY CATFISH! WIDOW JASPERS WAS UGLIER'N HOMEMADE SIN!

SHE HAD A FACE THAT COULD CURDLE MILK!

SHE COULD MAKE A HAINT HUG A THORN BUSH!

SHE HAD A FACE THAT COULD TURN A FREIGHT TRAIN UP A DIRT ROAD!

'COURSE, BEAUTY'S ONLY SKIN DEEP!

— BUT COLORFUL INSULTS RUN ON FOREVER!

THE DEARLY DEPARTED WIDOW JASPERS, AS EVERYONE KNOWS, WAS NO GREAT BEAUTY...

...IN FACT, SHE HAD A FACE THAT COULD RUN A BULLDOG OFF A MEATWAGON!

SHE COULD STOP A SACK OF TEN-EIGHT-EIGHT FERTILIZER IN MID-AIR!

SHE WAS SO UGLY, WHY, EVEN MADE UP SHE LOOKED LIKE A FROG STARING THROUGH A BLOCK OF ICE!

PREACHER, I WAS SHOCKED AT WHAT YOU SAID ABOUT WIDOW JASPERS IN HER EULOGY!

...THAT SHE HAD A HEART OF GOLD BUT A FACE THAT COULD CURDLE MILK!

SHAME ON YOU! REMARKING ON HER PHYSICAL APPEARANCE WHICH SHE COULD NOT HELP! THAT'S BLATANT LOOKS-ISM! AND YOU SHOULD KNOW BETTER! FOR SHAME!

WHEW!

SHE COULD HAUNT A NINE-ROOM HOUSE FROM ACROSS THE STREET!

PREACHER, I SEE YOU'RE STILL CALLING YOUR CONGREGATION "SINNERS"... TSK-TSK-TSK!

HOW MANY TIMES DO I HAVE TO TELL YOU?... "PEOPLE OF FOIBLES"!...

IDA MAE, IT'S HARD TO PREACH HELLFIRE AND DAMNATION WITHOUT USING THE WORD "SINNERS"!

— WHICH REMINDS ME: "HECKFIRE AND DARNATION"!

KNOCK KNOCK

PREACHER, I JUST CAME FROM THE MALL AND... AND I'M TROUBLED!...

WHAT'S THE MATTER, VERANDA?

ISN'T CHRISTMAS SUPPOSED TO BE A SPECIAL TIME OF YEAR?!...

YES.

MARLETTE

WELL, IT'S LOSING IT SPECIALNESS TO ME!...

I SEE...HOW SENSITIVE OF YOU TO NOTICE... YOU MEAN THE CRASS COMMERCIALISM ERODES ITS SPECIALNESS.

I MEAN, BIG DEAL! I SHOP LIKE THIS ALL YEAR LONG!

ASHES TO ASHES...
DUST TO DUST...

CUT! CUT!
PREACHER, COULD
YOU REPEAT THAT
LOUDER AND WITH
A BIT MORE
SINCERITY !?!

...AND LOSE
THE HAT,
WOULD YOU?!

I HATE
FUNERAL
VIDEOS!

I'M AFRAID I HAVE
AN ANNOUNCEMENT
I WISH I DIDN'T
HAVE TO MAKE...

I'M SORRY, BUT
I REFUSE TO
BAPTIZE ANOTHER
LAWYER IN THIS
BAPTISMAL POOL!

SO
SUE
ME!

LAWYERS
ALWAYS
LEAVE A
RING!

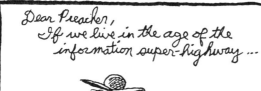

Dear Preacher,
If we live in the age of the
information super-highway...

...your column is a dead-end street!

THERE'S DEFINITELY
BEEN A DROP-OFF IN
THE NUMBER OF
CANDIDATES FOR
BAPTISM LATELY!

SOME HAVE
SUGGESTED IT
REFLECTS AN
EROSION OF MY
AUTHORITY AND
LACK OF CONFIDENCE
IN MY LEADERSHIP!

PERHAPS I SHOULD
LEAVE MY MR. QUACKERS
HOME IN THE TUB!

123

LET ME GET THIS STRAIGHT—THE WORD "SINNERS" IS SPIRITUALLY INCORRECT!

YOU GOT IT!

"PEOPLE OF FOIBLES" IS MORE SENSITIVE, SUPPORTIVE AND NURTURING!

I SEE.

PEOPLE OF FOIBLES, REPENT!

"REPENT" IS TOO HARSH—HOW ABOUT "REFLECT"?... "RECONSIDER"?..."TAKE A LOOK AT"?...

"CHECK IT OUT"?

PREACHER, YOU'RE A MUSEUM OF SPIRITUAL INCORRECTNESS!

YIKES!

YOUR USE OF GENDER-SPECIFIC DESCRIPTIONS OF THE DEITY IS TOTALLY UNACCEPTABLE!

FOR INSTANCE, "OUR FATHER WHO ART IN HEAVEN"...

YEAH?

"OUR PARENT OR GUARDIAN WHO ART IN HEAVEN"!...

OF COURSE!

"OUR PARENT WHO ART IN HEAVEN..."

NOW YOU'RE SPIRITUALLY CORRECT!

MUCH BETTER.

ANY OTHER SUGGESTIONS?

ACTUALLY, YOUR USE OF THE WORD "HYMN"...

LET ME GUESS—"HER'N!"

BINGO!

DEAR PREACHER, HOW DO YOU DEFINE "GOD"? THEOLOGIAN

Dear Theologian, The Holy is greater than the sum of Its parts.

MARLETTE

I'VE FINISHED MY SERMON MAKING THE ARGUMENT FOR *BAPTISM BY IMMERSION!*

MARLETTE

NOW ALL I NEED IS A SNAPPY TITLE!

"COME HELL OR HIGH WATER"!

PREACHER, MAMA SAYS I CAN GET MY LIPS IMPLANTED WITH COLLAGEN IF YOU SAY IT'S ALL RIGHT.

WHY ON EARTH WOULD YOU WANT TO DO THAT?

MADONNA DID!

MARLETTE

THE BLONDE LEADING THE BLONDE!

I HATE PLAYING THESE ATHEISTS!

THEY CONTEST EVERY FOUL!

HOW DID THEY GET IN THE *CHURCH LEAGUE* ANYWAY?!

THEY DON'T BELIEVE IN REFEREES!

MARLETTE

127

128

HAVE YOU THOUGHT ABOUT YOUR VOCATION, BOY?

WHEN I GROW UP I WANT TO BE A *WRITER!*

GOOD FOR YOU, KUDZU!

BUT ALL MY FRIENDS WANT TO BE *ANCHORMEN* OR *GAME SHOW HOSTESSES* OR *MTV VEEJAYS!...*

WHAT'S WRONG WITH ME, PREACHER?

NOT A THING, SON!...

© 1993 Creators Syndicate, Inc.

YOU'RE LOOKING BEYOND THE SHALLOW AND SUPERFICIAL FOR A CAREER THAT'S *SUBSTANTIAL* AND *MEANINGFUL!...*

I GUESS...

MARLETTE

PLUS, I WANT A LOW *HAIR-MAINTENANCE* PROFESSION!

PASCAL SAID ALL OF MAN'S TROUBLE COMES FROM HIS INABILITY TO SIT IN A ROOM BY HIMSELF!

UNCLE DUB SAID ALL OF HIS TROUBLES CAME FROM HIS INABILITY TO SIT IN A ROOM WITH HIS FIRST WIFE!

...AND NOW LET US ALL LIFT OUR VOICES IN SONG WITH "ROCK OF AGES"!...

BUMP-BUMP BOMP! BUMP-BUMP BOMP! BUMP-BUMP BOMP! BUMP-BUMP BOMP!

WEEE WIIIILLL WEEE WILLL ROCK YOU!

I GOTTA GET A NEW CONGREGATION!

≷SIGH≷

WHAT'S WRONG, BOY? YOU IN A FUNK AGAIN?

YEAH! I'VE BEEN THIS WAY SINCE CHRISTMAS!

POST-HOLIDAY LET-DOWN! YOU'LL GET OVER IT!

CHRISTMAS, 1986!

DADDY BEATS ME!...

MOMMA BEATS ME!...

I WANNA BE ADOPTED BY YOUR CHURCH LEAGUE BASKETBALL TEAM!...

WHY?

THEY DON'T BEAT NOBODY!

I MUST SAY, PREACHER, YOUR ATTITUDE IS NOT VERY SUPPORTIVE AND PASTORLY...

...JUST BECAUSE I LOST A SILLY GAME BY TAKING A BAD SHOT AND MISSING THE RIM, THE BACKBOARD AND EVERYTHING...

YOU SHOULD BE MORE FORGIVING! THINK WHAT THE LORD WOULD SAY!

"AIR BALL!... AIR BALL!... AIR BALL!..."

LORD, I WANT TO PRAY FOR OUR MISSIONARIES IN NIGERIA...

..THAT THEY MIGHT PREACH THY WORD...

... SAVE COUNTLESS SOULS...

... AND FIND ME A SEVEN-FOOT CENTER FOR MY CHURCH LEAGUE BASKETBALL TEAM!

PREACHER, YOU'RE STILL USING THAT WORD "SINNERS" INSTEAD OF THE SPIRITUALLY CORRECT "PEOPLE OF FOIBLES"...

YOU KNOW IT'S LOADED WITH NEGATIVE CULTURAL BIAS...

...IT'S NON-SUPPORTIVE, NON-NURTURING...

...IT MAKES YOUR CONGREGATION FEEL BAD ABOUT THEMSELVES AND DAMAGES THEIR SELF-ESTEEM!

I- I GUESS I'M JUST A PERSON OF FOIBLES!

DON'T MOCK ME!

I LOVE PLAYING THE UNITARIANS!

HOLY ROLLERS

THEY BELIEVE IN THE INNATE TALENT OF EACH OF THEIR PLAYERS...

...THEY HAVE DEEP AMBIVALENCE ABOUT WINNING...

... AND WHEN THEY LOSE, THEY ALWAYS BLAME IT ON THE UNFAIRNESS OF THE RULES!

"CELEBRITY PROZAC"?!

YES, IT'S MY NEW GOSSIP COLUMN FOR "MODERN DEPRESSION" MAGAZINE...

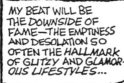

MY BEAT WILL BE THE DOWNSIDE OF FAME—THE EMPTINESS AND DESOLATION SO OFTEN THE HALLMARK OF GLITZY AND GLAMOROUS LIFESTYLES...

HOW BEING FABULOUS DOESN'T HELP YOU GET UP IN THE MORNING...

PLUS, I'LL BE HYPING ALL THE LATEST MOOD BRIGHTENER DRUGS THE STARS TURN TO FOR RELIEF FROM THEIR ENNUI AND DESPAIR!

HAVE YOU SEEN NASAL'S NEW GOSSIP COLUMN IN MODERN DEPRESSION MAGAZINE?

"CELEBRITY PROZAC"?

AMAZING THE NUMBER OF CELEBS WHO ARE SERIOUSLY DEPRESSED!

—AND THE ONES ON MEDICATION! ROCK STARS, TALK SHOW HOSTS, POLITICIANS, NEWS ANCHORS, NOVELISTS, MOVIE STARS!...

LOOK—THE ENTIRE OP-ED PAGE OF THE NEW YORK TIMES!

WELL, THAT FIGURES!

ACCORDING TO MODERN DEPRESSION'S "CELEBRITY PROZAC" COLUMN, MISERY IS RAMPANT IN THE ENTERTAINMENT INDUSTRY...

NO ONE'S SAFE!

THEY'RE IN DESPAIR AT DISNEY.

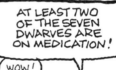

AT LEAST TWO OF THE SEVEN DWARVES ARE ON MEDICATION!

WOW!

SO THAT EXPLAINS DOPEY...

NOT TO MENTION HAPPY!

ACCORDING TO THE "CELEBRITY PROZAC" COLUMN IN MODERN DEPRESSION, TWO OF THE SEVEN DWARVES AT DISNEY ARE ON MEDICATION!

NO WAY!

HAPPY AND DOPEY!

OUTRAGEOUS! WHO PUT 'EM ON DRUGS?

DOC!

137

ACCORDING TO "CELEBRITY PROZAC," THE NEW GOSSIP COLUMN IN *MODERN DEPRESSION* MAGAZINE, A LOT OF OUR BIGGEST STARS ARE CLINICALLY DEPRESSED!...

—AND THE ONES ON MEDICATION!... THE NUMBERS ARE STAGGERING!

MOVIE STARS, ROCK STARS, SPORTS STARS!...

THE ENTIRE DEFENSIVE LINE OF THE BUFFALO BILLS...

...TALK SHOW HOSTS, NEWS ANCHORS, JOURNALISTS...

THE OP-ED PAGE OF THE NEW YORK TIMES...

...THE MAC NEIL-LEHRER NEWSHOUR, NPR'S ALL THINGS CONSIDERED!...

THIS READS LIKE A WHO'S WHO OF WHO'S BEEN SEDATED!

"CELEBRITY PROZAC" SAYS DISNEY'S BEEN RAVAGED BY DEPRESSION! MICKEY MOUSE HAS BEEN SUICIDAL SINCE THE EURO-DISNEY DISASTER!

GOOFY, DOPEY, HAPPY—THEY'RE ALL ON MEDICATION!

DONALD DUCK'S ON PROZAC!... HE'S HAD A MENTAL MAKE-OVER... CHANGED HIS NAME TO MELLO MALLARD!... SINGS 'ZIPPETY DOO DAH' ALL DAY LONG!

THEY'RE GONNA REMAKE "BEAUTY AND THE BEAST"! CALL IT "BEAUTY AND A GUY WITH MISFIRING NEURO-TRANSMITTERS"!

I MIGHT AS WELL FACE IT, PREACHER—THE SIZZLE'S GONE OUT OF MY MARRIAGE!

HAVE YOU TRIED SEDUCTION?

OH, YES— I TRIED PUTTING THE MOVES ON MY HUSBAND LAST NIGHT...

HE CALLED 911!

AS WE ALL KNOW, OUR DEAR DEPARTED BROTHER RALPH LIVED IN A BAD NEIGHBORHOOD...

NO RADIO

139

THIS CONGREGATION IS A TOUGH AUDIENCE...

SOME MINISTERS START OFF THEIR SERMONS WITH A LITTLE JOKE...

WITH THIS CROWD, I JUST SET PHASERS ON "STUN"!

Dear Preacher,
What will Eternity be like?
Wondering

Dear Wondering,
It will be like the Academy Awards hosted by Regis and Kathie Lee. Only shorter.

HOLY CATFISH! WE BLEW THAT GAME! WE HAD IT, AND WE GAVE IT AWAY!

WE SHOULD CHANGE OUR TEAM NAME FROM THE HOLY ROLLERS TO THE ARTICHOKES!

ARTICHOKES?

WE'VE ELEVATED CHOKING TO AN ARTFORM!

THE CATHOLICS' SEVEN-FOOT CENTER IS EATING US ALIVE!

NOW LISTEN UP! WHICH ONE OF YOU GUYS CAN STOP HIM DEFENSIVELY?!

ME! ME! ME!

MEEEEEEE! ♪♪♪

NEVER RECRUIT A GOSPEL QUARTET TO PLAY CHURCH LEAGUE BASKETBALL!

143

THAT NEW PLAYER ON THE QUAKERS' TEAM LOOKS PRETTY INTIMIDATING!

RELAX—HE'S BIG, BUT HE'S PRETTY ONE-DIMENSIONAL! HE'S ONLY DEVELOPED ONE ASPECT OF HIS GAME!

— MONSTER DUNKS!

PREACHER, WHAT WAS EVERYBODY CHANTING AT ME WHEN I MISSED MY FREE THROW?

"HEIMLICH!... HEIMLICH!... HEIMLICH!..." AS IN "HEIMLICH MANEUVER"!

HEIMLICH MANEUVER? WHAT FOR?!

YOU CHOKED!

LISTEN TO THAT CROWD! BOY, THESE UNITARIANS SURE ARE INTELLECTUALS!

...AND THEY DON'T LET YOU FORGET IT!

ATMOSPHERIC SPHEROID! ATMOSPHERIC SPHEROID!

SAY WHAT?

AIR BALL! AIR BALL!

IT'S SO HUMILIATING TO BE BENCHED IN CHURCH LEAGUE BASKETBALL!...

ACTUALLY, BENCHING WOULDN'T BE SO BAD...

... BUT IN CHURCH LEAGUE, YOU'RE PEWED!

144

146

I NOW PRONOUNCE YOU HUSBAND AND WIFE!

LOOK AT THOSE TWO LOVEBIRDS DANCING — ISN'T THAT SWEET!

GOOD JOB, PREACHER! AS FATHER OF THE BRIDE I WANT YOU TO HAVE THIS — JUST A LITTLE SOMETHING FOR YOUR TROUBLE...

AW, HUSH NOW, WILBUR — I DON'T EXPECT ANYTHING FOR MY SERVICES...

JUST BEING A PART OF BRINGING THOSE TWO TOGETHER FOR A LIFETIME OF HAPPINESS IS PAYMENT ENOUGH FOR ME!

IF YOU SAY SO, PREACHER...

OF COURSE, TWO OUTA THREE MARRIAGES DO END IN DIVORCE!

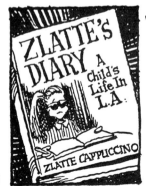

153

155

WHAT ARE YOU READING?

"INANITY FAIR."

THAT'S THE MAGAZINE WITH ALL THE INSERTS AND ADS FOR SCENTS AND FRAGRANCES AND PERFUMES...

DO YOU SUBSCRIBE?

NO, I HAVE A RULE:

NEVER SUBSCRIBE TO ANYTHING THAT SMELLS BETTER THAN IT READS!

YOU OUGHTA COME TO CHURCH THIS SUNDAY, DUB...

I'M GONNA PREACH ON EVERLASTING TORMENT!

OH, I GET IT—SHOW AND TELL!

HEY, THIS NEW TV SHOW, "CELEBRITY CANINGS," IS WILDLY POPULAR...

LAST WEEK, IT SET A RATINGS RECORD...

DREW BARRYMORE WAS GUEST HOST...

...AND CANED HERSELF!

WHAT DO YOU THINK OF GENERATION X?

GENERATION X?

YOU KNOW—THE LOST, ALIENATED GENERATION THAT CAME ALONG AFTER THE BABY BOOMERS... THEY HAVE NO IDENTITY—THAT'S WHY IT'S CALLED GENERATION X.

I THOUGHT IT WAS BECAUSE THEY CAN'T SIGN THEIR OWN NAMES!

156

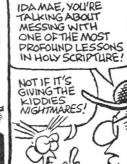

POOR OL' LES! WE COULDN'T LIFT THE COFFIN!

HAD TO SEND FOR MORE PALL BEARERS!

WE UNDER-ESTIMATED HIS GIRTH!

APPARENTLY, LES IS MORE!

WHAT IS THE ANSWER, PREACHER?

WELL, SON, WHEN I WANT AN ANSWER, YOU KNOW WHERE I TURN...

OPRAH?

CLOSE— BUT NO CIGAR!

THE BOBBITT CHANNEL...THE BUTTAFUOCO CHANNEL...

¿CLICK¿

...THE TONYA HARDING CHANNEL... THE MENENDEZ BROTHERS CHANNEL...

¿CLICK¿
¿CLICK¿

...THE PAULA JONES CHANNEL... AND NOW THE O.J. CHANNEL!...

¿CLICK¿
¿CLICK¿

MAYBE I'LL JUST RENT A VIDEO!

JOEY BUTTAFUOCO WAS RELEASED FROM PRISON TODAY IN THE CUSTODY OF LORENA BOBBITT...

...MEANWHILE, THE MENENDEZ BROTHERS DENIED ATTENDING THE FUNERAL OF RICHARD NIXON WITH TONYA HARDING, WHO WAS SEEN AT JACKIE O'S FUNERAL ESCORTED BY MICHAEL JACKSON...

PAULA JONES COULD NOT BE REACHED FOR COMMENT BECAUSE SHE WAS TRAPPED IN A WHITE BRONCO ON THE L.A. FREEWAY WITH O.J. SIMPSON! FILM AT ELEVEN!

I GET ALL MY EXERCISE ON THE NEWS CYCLE!

MY GUEST TODAY IS FIRST FAMILY THERAPIST AND *SECRETARY OF FEELINGS*, DR. NATHAN GOODVIBES

NATHAN, YOU'VE JUST RETURNED FROM A NOSTALGIA TRIP BILLED AS PERHAPS THE SINGLE MOST SIGNIFICANT GATHERING OF THIS GENERATION—AN EVENT YOU HELPED ORGANIZE!

THAT'S RIGHT, REVEREND—"MOODSTOCK"! A FESTIVAL OF *INNER PEACE*, SHARING AND NETWORKING!

SEX, DRUGS AND ROCK AND ROLL!?

CONDOMS, PROZAC AND MUZAK!

SO WHAT WAS IT LIKE AT "MOODSTOCK"?

THREE DAYS OF *INNER PEACE, SELF ESTEEM* AND *EASY LISTENING!*

TELL US A LITTLE ABOUT THE MUSIC!

IT WAS AWESOME—THE SOUNDS OF OUR GENERA-TION!

"COUNTRY JOE AND THE SUSHI"!... "TONY ROBBINS 'AND THE MIRACLES"!...

"CROSBY, STILLS, ERNST AND YOUNG"!

WHAT WERE SOME OF THE HIGH POINTS OF MOODSTOCK FOR YOU, NATHAN GOODVIBES?

THE GROUP HUGS, DEFINITELY!...AND THERE WERE REPORTS OF A COUPLE OF *REBIRTHINGS!*

BY THE WAY, INNER CHILD DAY CARE WAS PROVIDED! LET'S SEE... HIGH POINTS?... THERE WAS THE SENSITIVE MAN'S PONYTAIL COMPETITION!

ROBERT BLY'S TWENTY MINUTE DRUM SOLO!... I'VE NEVER HEARD SUCH A SPARE, SOULFUL "INNA GADDA DAVIDA"!

...AND OF COURSE SCOTT PECK'S LECTURE ON "THE INFORMATION HIGHWAY LESS TRAVELED"!

SOUNDS LIKE "MOODSTOCK" WAS A DEFINING MOMENT FOR THE BOOMER GENERA-TION!

FER SHUR!

SUCH SUPPOR-TIVENESS!...SUCH RESONATING!... SUCH NETWORKING OPPORTUNITIES!... YOU HAD TO BE THERE!

—AND HOW MANY ACTUALLY WERE THERE?!

NOBODY WAS ALL THERE... BECAUSE OF THE PROZAC...

...BUT *TECHNICALLY* HALF A MILLION STRONG!

YOU HAD TO BE THERE, PREACHER—"WOODSTOCK" WAS IDYLLIC BLISS FOR US BABY BOOMERS!...

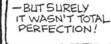

—BUT SURELY IT WASN'T TOTAL PERFECTION!

YOU'RE REFERRING TO THE "BAD GUAC" INCIDENT!

I HEARD SOMEONE "OD'D"!

IT'S TRUE—THERE WAS SOME BROWN GUACAMOLE GOING AROUND...

BUMMER!

PREACHER, YOUR SCRIPTURE LESSONS ARE WAY TOO VIOLENT!...

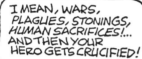

I MEAN, WARS, PLAGUES, STONINGS, HUMAN SACRIFICES!... AND THEN YOUR HERO GETS CRUCIFIED!

IDA MAE, SUFFERING IS KIND OF CENTRAL TO THE FAITH!

FINE—LET 'EM EAT AIRPLANE FOOD!

...AND DO YOU, LISA MARIE, TAKE MICHAEL TO BE YOUR LAWFUL WEDDED HUSBAND?

I DO.

WE CARTOON PREACHERS MARRY ALL THE CARTOON COUPLES!

REALLY, PREACHER?... YOU ACTUALLY PERFORMED THE CEREMONY?

YES, INDEED!

BRRR! I CAN'T THINK OF A CREEPIER PAIRING THAN MICHAEL JACKSON AND LISA MARIE PRESLEY!

DAN RATHER AND CONNIE CHUNG!

OH, THE MICHAEL-LISA MARIE WEDDING WAS A STAR-STUDDED EVENT ALL RIGHT!

ALL THE DISNEY STARS WERE THERE: MICKEY, MINNIE, DONALD, GOOFY, DOPEY... AND, OF COURSE, ELVIS WAS THERE... AND LIZ...

MARLETTE

LIZ WAS IN TEARS THE WHOLE TIME.

IT WAS THE FIRST TIME SHE'D BEEN TO A WEDDING WHERE SHE WASN'T THE *BRIDE!*

ALL IN ALL, THE MICHAEL AND LISA MARIE CEREMONY WAS ONE OF THE LOVELIEST I'VE PERFORMED!

MARLETTE

OF COURSE, THERE WAS ONE UGLY INCIDENT...

LIZ AND *ELVIS* FIGHTING OVER THE LAST SLICE OF WEDDING CAKE!

AS YOU KNOW, THERE'S BEEN A LOT OF CRITICISM OF *MICHAEL AND LISA MARIE* FOR MARRYING!

IF I HEARD IT ONCE, I HEARD IT A THOUSAND TIMES: "THAT SKINNY WHITE GIRL DON'T KNOW WHAT SHE'S DOING!"

MARLETTE

—AND YOU SHOULD HEAR WHAT THEY SAY ABOUT *LISA MARIE!*

IT WAS A BEAUTIFUL CEREMONY...

ELVIS GAVE AWAY LISA MARIE...

DIANA ROSS GAVE AWAY MICHAEL...

THEN ALL THE JACKSONS TRIED TO GIVE AWAY LATOYA!

MARLETTE

ELVIS GAVE THE BRIDE AWAY, NATURALLY, BUT THERE WAS A LOT OF CONTROVERSY OVER WHO WOULD BE THE BEST MAN!

WE'RE TALKING THE JACKSONS HERE, SO AS YOU CAN IMAGINE, THERE WAS SOME QUIBBLING...

SO WHO GOT BEST MAN — TITO ?!?

NO...

— THE PET MONKEY.

MARLETTE

AH, BUT THERE WILL COME A DAY, BROTHERS AND SISTERS, WHEN THE SHEEP ARE SEPARATED FROM THE GOATS!...

...THE WHEAT FROM THE CHAFF!...

MARLETTE

...REGIS FROM KATHIE LEE!

MARRIAGE COUNSELOR

IF HE SNAPS AND CRACKLES ONE MORE TIME, I'M GONNA POP HIM!

MARLETTE

ROSEANNE AND TOM ARNOLD!... LORENA AND JOHN BOBBITT!...

HOLY CATFISH! SOME OF MY MOST FAMOUS UNIONS HAVE BITTEN THE DUST!

PEOPLE ARE STARTING TO TALK!

MARLETTE

THEY SAY REV. DUNN IS TO LOVE AS DR. KEVORKIAN IS TO HEALING!

163

R-RING!

HELLO?

I KNEW YOU'D SAY THAT!

WHO IS THIS? —AND I KNEW YOU'D SAY THAT, TOO!

I HATE THE PSYCHIC FRIENDS NETWORK!

PREACHER, I'M HAVING SECOND THOUGHTS ABOUT MY CAREER CHOICE!

AS YOU KNOW, I'VE ALWAYS WANTED TO BE A MODEL—BUT NOW I SEE THAT AS PRETTY SHALLOW AND SUPERFICIAL!...

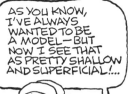

GOOD FOR YOU, CHILD.

NOW I WANT TO BE A SUPER MODEL!

...NOW ALL IN FAVOR OF BURNING BOOKS...

...WITCH HUNTS AT OUR SEMINARIES...

...AND CUTTING OFF FUNDS FOR PROGRAMS THAT DON'T SEEM TO SQUARE WITH OUR NARROW DOCTRINAL VIEWS...

...RAISE YOUR WEBBED FINGERS!

Dear Ms. Goodvibes, How can we tell kids to "Just Say No" to drugs...

...but celebrate prescription "mood brighteners" as a cure for depression? Confused

Dear Confused, You've got to separate the *amateurs* from the Prozac.

164

I READ THAT YOUR OLD BIBLE COLLEGE BUDDY, REV. JERRY JEFF JEETER, JUST GOT OUT OF PRISON!
ALREADY?
NO, HE'S COMPLETELY REHABILITATED! HE SPENT ALL THAT TIME IN PRISON STUDYING THE SCRIPTURES!
I'LL BET.
MARLETTE
LOOKING FOR LOOPHOLES!

UNFAIR, UMP!
CAN YOU BELIEVE THAT?!
MARLETTE
WE'RE PLAYING THE JESUITS, AND THE UMPIRE IS CATHOLIC!
SHEESH!
HOW DO YOU KNOW?
HE JUST EXCOMMUNICATED ME FROM THE BALLGAME!

I HATE PLAYING THE JESUITS...
MARLETTE
THEY CONTEST EVERY CALL!
YEP...
...BEFORE THE GAME, I HAD TO LISTEN TO 'EM FOR A HALF AN HOUR...
...DEBATE THE EMPIRICAL VERSUS THE ONTOLOGICAL PROOF FOR THE EXISTENCE OF THE UMPIRE!

BOY, ARE THOSE TRAPPISTS ARROGANT!
THEY THINK THEY'VE GOT THIS TOURNAMENT IN THE BAG!
THEY'RE COCKY ALL RIGHT!...
MARLETTE
WHEN I TOLD 'EM GOD IS ON OUR SIDE...
...THEY SAID, "FINE- YOU CAN HAVE 'IM, AND WE'LL SPOT YOU TEN POINTS!"

THOSE TRAPPISTS ARE A BUNCH OF BIG SHOWOFFS!

THEY'RE DISCIPLINED ALL RIGHT—YOU MEAN THE GREGORIAN INFIELD CHATTER!?

THE *ILLUMINATED* STAT SHEETS!

HEY, I MADE A MISTAKE! SO SUE ME! SHEESH!

I THINK I JUST COMMITTED A FAUX PAS...

SEE THAT CONFESSIONAL BOOTH NEXT TO THE TRAPPISTS' DUGOUT?

I THOUGHT IT WAS A *PORT-A-JOHN!*

HEY, BROTHER ANSELM! YOUR CASSOCK'S ON BACKWARDS!

WHEN YOU'VE TAKEN A VOW OF SILENCE, TRASHTALK IS QUITE A CHALLENGE!

"I'M O.J.—YOU'RE O.J." IS THE FIRST SELF-HELP BOOK TO DEAL WITH THE DARK SIDE OF OUR INNER CELEB...

THE ROSEANNE BARR WITHIN... THE SHANNEN DOHERTY...THE JOEY BUTTAFUOCO..... OUR INNER LORENA BOBBITT...

WHAT HAPPENED TO OUR *INNER CHILD?*

IT WAS KNEE-CAPPED BY OUR *INNER TONYA HARDING!*

169

171

175

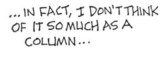

177

178

Dear Mr. Goodvibes,
I am a sensitive male, in touch with my feminine side.

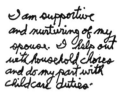

I am supportive and nurturing of my spouse. I help out with household chores and do my part with childcare duties.

I even took my wife's maiden name, but she says I'm still insensitive.

I'm afraid if I get any more sensitive, I will mildew and rot!

Dear Mr. Goodvibes, I don't get it.

My friend had an asthma attack, and they took him to the hospital...

I had a panic attack, and they threw me in jail!

"... AND THOUGH I MAY SPEAK WITH THE TONGUES OF MEN AND ANGELS AND HAVE NOT CHARITY..."

"... I AM ABOUT ONE HUSHPUPPY SHORT OF A BARBECUE PLATTER!"

PAUL'S LETTER TO THE CAROLINIANS!

I SAW A GREAT ACTION/BUDDY MOVIE LAST NIGHT STARRING ALAN ALDA AND GENE WILDER!...

ALAN ALDA?... GENE WILDER?...

"REVENGE OF THE SENSITIVE MALES IN TOUCH WITH THEIR FEMININE SIDES"!

179

Dear Santa, Have I been good this year?

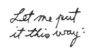
Let me put it this way:

All I want for Christmas is unwaxed dental floss.

MARLETTE

LOVE MEANS NEVER HAVING TO SAY YOU'RE SORRY...

...YOU DIDN'T SIGN A PRE-NUPTIAL AGREEMENT!

MARLETTE

WHAT WAS IT LIKE WHEN YOU WERE CALLED TO GO INTO THE MINISTRY, PREACHER?

WAS IT A DAMASCUS ROAD EXPERIENCE?

MORE LIKE A DAMASCUS ROADKILL EXPERIENCE.

MARLETTE

Dear Santa, Have I been good this year?

I worked hard for animal rights...

...lobbying to abolish windshields to stop the senseless slaughter of moths and june bugs on our nation's highways...

MARLETTE

...which brings me to the little matter of your treatment of the reindeer...

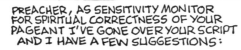

183

184

185

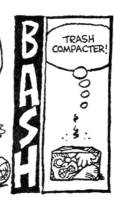

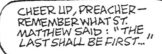

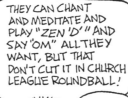